MOLLIE HEMENS

Reaching Out

Four Play Scripts for the Classroom

Activities linked to the National Curriculum by
Mollie Hemens

Heinemann Educational Publishers
Halley Court, Jordan Hill, Oxford OX2 8EJ
A division of Reed Educational and Professional Publishing Ltd

MELBOURNE AUCKLAND
FLORENCE PRAGUE MADRID ATHENS
SINGAPORE TOKYO SÃO PAULO
PORTSMOUTH NH MEXICO CITY
IBADAN GABORONE JOHANNESBURG
KAMPALA NAIROBI

First published 1998

2002 2001 2000 99 98

10 9 8 7 6 5 4 3 2 1

ISBN 0 435 23324 6

Original design by Jeffrey White Creative Associates; adapted by Jim Turner
Typeset by ⊼ Tek-Art, Croydon, Surrey
Cover illustration by Benjamin Russell Warner
Cover design by Aricot Vert
Printed and bound in the United Kingdom by Clays Ltd, St Ives plc

CONTENTS

NOTES TO TEACHERS

About the Play Scripts

Reaching Out is a set of four play scripts about a group of Year Nine pupils during the Summer Term before they move on to Year Ten and their GCSE courses. The plays explore such issues as ambitions for the future, making choices, friendship, loyalty, bullying and caring about others. Although each play stands alone, if read in order there is also an overall build-up of plot and characterization which culminates in the final play. These play scripts are designed for classroom use and therefore the stage directions are written in a narrative style. However, the plays can also be used to equal effect in the Drama Studio. The Speaking and Listening and Writing activities, at the back of the book, are based on the requirements of the National Curriculum, Key Stage 3.

Activities

The author's experience has shown that pupils' written work is of a significantly higher quality when based on oral activities directly linked to that written work. All activities, therefore, begin with Speaking and Listening and are followed by Writing.

Pupils should be encouraged to make notes on the Oral Activities performed by the rest of the class, so that they can choose to write about an activity which they have not prepared themselves. However, whether or not the activities are used in whole or in part, they are a valuable resource fulfilling the oral and written criteria of the National Curriculum, Key Stage 3, including the study of play scripts.

Help Notes

There are Help Notes at the back of the book. These make it possible for a variety of different activities, which reflect the full range of pupils' interests and abilities, to be going on in the classroom at the same time.

About the Author

Mollie Hemens has extensive experience of teaching English in the Secondary sector and is a former Head of Drama. She is co-author of *Stepping Up*, four short plays based around Year Seven. She also works as a consultant on teacher development courses.

Louise

List of Characters

Year Nine pupils
Louise
Natalie
Sonia
Steve
Stuart
Clinton
Gordon
Andy

Teachers
Mr Kingston, French/PE
Miss Wright, Food Technology
Mrs Powers, Form Tutor
Mr Freeman, Deputy Head

Parents
Mary, Steve's Gran
Angie, Steve's Mum
Tina, Louise's Mum

LOUISE

Scene One

*Characters: Louise, Natalie, Sonia, Steve,
Mr Kingston, Mr Freeman.*

*Before school, the first day of the Summer Term.
On a corridor, where the Deputy Head, Mr Freeman,
has his office. Two Year Nine pupils, Sonia and
Natalie, are waiting for their friend, Louise.*

Natalie Where's Louise? She said she'd meet us early,
before Registration.

Sonia Don't know. I knocked for her but there was no
reply. She must have gone somewhere.

Natalie I'm starving already and it's only half past eight.

Sonia Didn't you have any breakfast?

Natalie No. And you're not to give me any food. I've got to
lose weight. I'm so fat.

*Sonia is only half-listening. She peers down the
corridor and suddenly sees Louise.*

Sonia Louise! Over here! Where've you been? You're
nearly late.

Louise I'm glad I'm only nearly late. You said you'd knock
for me.

Sonia I did but you weren't in. You must have gone
somewhere.

Louise *Gone* somewhere? I sometimes wonder if you've
got a brain, Sonia. You didn't knock loud enough, so
I didn't hear you, so I didn't wake up. If it hadn't
been for my mum phoning, I'd still be in bed.

Natalie Ssh, you two. Here comes Mr Kingston.

She greets Mr Kingston.

Natalie   Hello, Sir.

Mr Kingston Hello, girls.

Natalie   Did you have a good holiday, Sir?

Mr Kingston Not bad, not bad. See you later in French.

Mr Kingston walks off down the corridor.

Natalie   Did you hear that? I hope I'm in his French group next year.

Louise   Take that stupid look off your face.

Louise and Sonia collapse into laughter.

Louise   Anyway, he fancies Miss Wright.

Natalie   How do you know?

Louise   (*scornfully*) Everyone knows that! They send messages to each other's classrooms and he runs out of chalk so he can visit her.

Sonia   I'm quite looking forward to being in Year Ten.

Louise   I'm going to give it my best shot, I want to do Business Studies at the college.

Natalie   That's two years away!

Louise   You have to plan ahead to get ahead.

Natalie   You'll have to buy yourself an alarm clock with a loud bell then.

She points to Louise's nails, which are painted bright pink.

Natalie   And you'll have to get some invisible nail polish!

Louise   Very funny.

Sonia   I bet Mrs Powers makes you take that polish off.

Louise   I expect she will. Still, it's cheaper than buying my own remover.

A bell rings.

Natalie   Come on, that's Registration.

They walk down the corridor. As they reach the office of the Deputy Head, Mr Freeman, the door opens.

Mr Freeman	Ah, Louise, perfect, just the person I was looking for. Have you got a minute?
Natalie	See you later. We'll explain to Mrs Powers why you aren't in Registration.
	Natalie and Sonia walk off down the corridor.
Mr Freeman	Come into my office a minute, would you?
	Louise enters the room. A boy is sitting hunched on a chair, staring moodily at the floor.
Mr Freeman	This is Steve Richards. He's new and he's going to be in your Registration group. Could you take him under your wing, show him the ropes, introduce him to your pals and so on?
Louise	Yes, Sir. Hi, Steve.
	Steve looks up and nods briefly at Louise.
Mr Freeman	Get back to me if there are problems. If I can't sort them out, Louise can.
Louise	Very funny, Sir.
	Louise and Steve leave the room and start to walk towards the Registration room.
Louise	So what brings you to our school?
Steve	Just moved into the area.
Louise	Do you know anybody yet?
Steve	No, I only moved last week.
Louise	What school were you at before?
Steve	Not one you'd know.
Louise	Have you managed to get all your subject choices for next year?
Steve	I'm not really bothered. School's a waste of time for what I want to do.
Louise	Oh, and what's that?
Steve	I'm going to be a bodyguard.
	Louise stops walking and looks at him in surprise.
Louise	Come again?

| **Steve** | Not just any bodyguard, a really famous person's bodyguard. |

Louise tries not to laugh.

Louise	Like a rock star, or the Prime Minister?
Steve	Rock star, I think.
Louise	That's interesting. I don't think I noticed any leaflets about it in the Careers Room.
Steve	I'm in training for it, so it doesn't really matter what courses I do here.

They reach the Registration room. Louise is still trying hard not to laugh.

Scene Two

Characters: Louise, Natalie, Sonia, Stuart, Gordon, Andy, Clinton, Steve.

The same day at morning break. In the Registration room. The girls are sitting on one side of the room and the boys are in a group nearby.

Natalie	That's really weird, if you ask me. A bodyguard!
Louise	I couldn't keep a straight face.
Natalie	Do you think he's for real?
Louise	He says he's got his own training programme.
Sonia	Perhaps he was trying to make a big impression on his first day.
Louise	Maybe. Ah well, whatever turns you on . . .
Sonia	There was a film I saw once about a black pop star and she had a white bodyguard and they fell in love and all that. Maybe that's where he got the idea from.

Natalie	(*giggling*) You never know, Louise, you might fall in love with the new boy and he can practise being your bodyguard.
Louise	Shut up, stupid! Getting a boyfriend, that's all you can ever think of.
	Gordon, Stuart, Andy and Clinton overhear the girls' conversation.
Stuart	Who's got a boyfriend?
Sonia	Natalie says the new boy might want to go out with Louise.
Louise	Shut up, Sonia! You're so brainless.
Gordon	What new boy?
Natalie	Steve Richards. Get this. He only told Louise he's going to be a bodyguard!
Gordon	(*in disbelief*) A what?
Louise	It's true. I was passing Mr Freeman's office, when he needed somebody to take the new boy to Registration. I was being friendly to him, you know, as you do.
Stuart	We know, don't we, lads?
	Stuart grins and winks at the others.
Louise	A one-track mind, that's what you lot have got. I was trying to make him feel welcome, you know, chatting, and he comes right out with, *'I'm going to be a bodyguard.'*
	They all laugh.
Louise	I didn't know what to say.
Gordon	I can't say as I've noticed him that much.
Natalie	That's because you don't notice anyone unless they're wearing football boots.
Louise	He's not bothered about what options he's going to do.
Andy	I wish I wasn't. I know I'm going to fail all of mine, I'm no good at anything.

Sonia   You're good at cooking. Don't you want to be a chef or something?

Stuart   Women's work!

Andy   Loads of chefs are men. Miss Wright told me when I signed up for GCSE Food Technology.

Louise   Does it matter? Girls' work, boys' work, there shouldn't be any difference.

Stuart   In which case, you can be my bodyguard. I think the position's vacant.

The boys laugh.

Clinton   Talking of bodyguards, here comes one now.

Steve enters the room. He pauses by the door and looks around.

Gordon   Steve, come over here. We were just discussing dangerous jobs. I understand you've got a bit of experience in that line.

They all laugh.

Steve   I don't know what you're talking about.

Stuart   Louise says you're going to be a bodyguard. Is it true?

Clinton   What qualifications do you need?

Steve   Mind your own business.

Stuart   That's not very friendly. We're just trying to make you welcome.

Louise   Okay, the joke's over.

Stuart   (*ignoring her*) Tell you what, I'll ask my mates in Year Eleven if they've got any openings for a bodyguard.

Sonia   You don't want to go mixing with his mates, Steve. They're really hard.

Natalie   And nothing but trouble.

Stuart   Do me a favour! You don't really think I'd want to hang around with somebody like him? I mean, just look at him, he's all skin and bone.

Stuart leans over and prods Steve on the arm. Steve pushes him away.

Steve   Get off!

Stuart, Gordon, Clinton and Andy burst out laughing. A bell rings.

Louise   Leave him alone! I wish I hadn't said anything now.

Natalie   Come on, Louise, let's go. They're not worth it.

The girls leave the room. The boys follow, pushing and shoving each other. Steve stands silently to one side, watching them. When they have gone, he picks up his bag and slowly follows them out.

Scene Three

Characters: Steve, Stuart, Gordon, Andy, Clinton, Mr Kingston.

Two weeks later. In the boys' Changing room. Steve is alone. Stuart, Gordon, Andy and Clinton enter noisily. They are wearing muddy football kit and are excited from the game.

Gordon   Call yourself a footballer? You couldn't kick a paper bag.

Clinton   I'll have you for that!

Clinton lunges forward and tackles Gordon to the ground, where they wrestle together. Stuart steps over them.

Stuart   If it isn't Steve, the bodyguard. You look nice and clean and fresh. Been practising guarding have you? See how you get on with my socks, you can guard them.

He takes his dirty socks off and throws them down by Steve's bag.

Stuart Make sure you look after them, they mean a lot to me. Not many people are as attached to their socks as I am. As a matter of fact, I'm so attached, I hardly take 'em off. Isn't that right, lads?

Gordon and Clinton stop wrestling and nod enthusiastically.

Stuart Gather round, and let's listen to what Steve has to tell us about bodyguarding.

The four boys crowd round Steve, who sits down on the bench.

Andy He's sitting on your socks, Stu.

Stuart So he is. You'll have to be a bit more careful, Steve. Look before you sit.

Gordon Shall I move him?

Stuart That's a kind thought, Gordon, but I'm sure Steve can move himself.

Steve Leave me alone!

Clinton Oh, he can talk.

Andy He's still sitting on your socks.

Stuart So he is. Are you going to move, Stevie boy, or shall I get my friends to help you?

Steve (*muttering*) I'll sit where I like.

Stuart Oh no, you won't. Gordon, Clinton, give him a hand.

Gordon and Clinton take hold of an arm and a leg each and lift Steve up. They drop him heavily to the floor.

Stuart That wasn't very friendly, Steve. I don't know how you'll get on as a bodyguard if you can't talk nicely to people.

Clinton Get him to tell me how to be a bodyguard. I fancy doing that. What qualifications do you need?

Stuart Not many, eh, Stevie?

Steve You don't know anything about it.

Stuart You can tell us then. We're not in a hurry.

Andy If you don't mind me saying, he doesn't look big enough. I mean, look at his arms.

Andy lifts Steve's arm and examines it for muscles.

Clinton Yeah, look at his chest.

Clinton prods Steve in the chest.

Stuart He needs a few lessons, that's all. Now, listen carefully, Steve. I want you to guard my socks. Gordon, get my socks.

Gordon gets the socks and holds them at arm's length.

Gordon They're a bit ripe!

Stuart Course they are. I told you, I'm very attached to them. Hold him still.

Gordon and Clinton hold Steve down. He begins to struggle and tries to turn away as Stuart ties the socks around his mouth.

Stuart Hold him!

He ties the socks around Steve's mouth.

Stuart Now get him to his feet. I think it's washday for my socks. He can guard them and wash them at the same time. Get him over to the wash basin. Andy, turn on the tap.

Gordon and Clinton drag a struggling Steve over to the wash basin, where Andy has turned the cold tap full on.

Stuart Turn him round and hold his head back.

Gordon and Clinton follow Stuart's orders. The water hits Steve's upturned face and Stuart rubs the socks into Steve's mouth with the palm of his hand.

Stuart Got to get them nice and clean.

Mr Kingston enters the Changing room.

Mr Kingston   What's going on here?

Andy turns off the tap, Gordon and Clinton let go of Steve, Stuart quickly unties the socks from around Steve's face.

Mr Kingston   Are you all right, lad?

Steve   (*mumbling*) Yes, Sir.

Mr Kingston turns to the others.

Mr Kingston   I want an explanation, and I want it now!

Stuart   We were having a muck about, weren't we, Steve?

Steve   Yeah, we were mucking about.

Mr Kingston   It certainly didn't seem that way to me. Look at him, he's soaking wet!

Steve   I'm all right. It's just a bit of water.

Mr Kingston   You're new aren't you? We can take this further, you know.

Steve   It was just a muck about, Sir.

Mr Kingston   (*doubtfully*) Well, if you're sure.

He turns to the others.

Mr Kingston   This floor's a mess, get it cleaned up. You'll find a bucket and mop in the caretaker's office.

Stuart   Yes, Sir. Andy, get the bucket.

Andy   I'm on my way!

Andy quickly leaves the Changing room.

Mr Kingston   Gordon, Clinton, pick up all the football kit. Get this place tidy.

Gordon   Yes, Sir.

Gordon and Clinton start to tidy the kit up.

Mr Kingston   Stuart, a word in your shell-like, if you please.

Mr Kingston and Stuart move away from Steve, who stands dejectedly staring at the floor.

Mr Kingston   No more, do you understand? This was more than a muck about. You know it and I know it. I'm warning you. If you pick on him again, you'll have me to deal with.

Stuart doesn't reply.

Mr Kingston   Did you hear me? This was a clear case of bullying and there'll be no more of it.

Mr Kingston glares at Stuart, who shrugs and looks away.

Scene Four

Characters: Mr Kingston, Mr Freeman, Mrs Powers.

The same day, after school. In the Staff room. Mr Kingston is recounting the incident in the Changing room to Mr Freeman and Mrs Powers.

Mr Kingston   It was more than joking around, but I can't prove it.

Mr Freeman   There's not a lot we can do if the boy insists that he wasn't being bullied.

Mr Kingston   I know, but it's such a familiar story, especially with boys. The bullies get away with it time after time, because the victims are too frightened to take a stand against them.

Mrs Powers   I have to say that I'm rather concerned about Steven. He does seem to be having problems settling in.

Mr Freeman   What's his attendance like? The report from his last school said that it was poor.

Mrs Powers   It's been excellent, so far. He hasn't missed a day.

Mr Kingston   What's the background?

Mr Freeman It seems that he was living with his mother and her boyfriend. There were problems and Steve moved in with Gran, who lives locally.

Mr Kingston Will we manage to keep him? He's a perfect target for the bullies.

Mrs Powers They're not bad kids. I think that given Steven's attitude, it was just too tempting for them. It sounds like it was a bit of a joke that got out of hand.

Mr Kingston Maybe the others but not Stuart. He's mixing with that hooligan Neil Fisher in Year Eleven and that can only mean he's picking up some very bad habits.

Mrs Powers I'd better have a word with them. Maybe that will stop the whole business.

Mr Kingston Nip it in the bud, you mean? I know what I'd nip, if I had my way. Those kids need a taste of their own medicine.

Mrs Powers Let me try things my way, first.

Mr Freeman Let me know how you get on. We need to keep a close eye on things.

Mr Kingston Well, I've got a football practice to take. I'll see you later.

Mr Kingston puts on his track suit jacket and leaves the room.

Scene Five

Characters: Louise, Natalie, Sonia, Stuart, Gordon, Clinton, Andy.

Two weeks later, before school. In the Registration room. Louise and Natalie are finishing off some homework. Stuart walks past them and knocks a book off their table.

Natalie Watch it!

Stuart Sorry, it was an accident. What are you doing anyway?

Stuart leans over the table and pushes the papers about.

Louise Pack it in! We haven't got much time left. This must be handed in first lesson.

Stuart backs away from the table in mock fright.

Stuart Please don't shout at me or I'll have to ask Mrs Powers to have a word with you.

The boys burst into loud laughter.

Natalie It wasn't *that* funny!

Louise Hadn't you noticed, Nat? They're Stuart's little helpers.

Clinton We stick together. Not like you girls, always falling out over something or another.

Natalie You think you're still at Infant school. *'Get Mrs Powers to have a word.'* How juvenile can you get?

Stuart Oh, but she will have a word with you, if I ask her, won't she lads?

Andy You should have heard her going on at us. I was nearly wetting myself.

Gordon It was a right laugh when Mrs Powers took us to one side and asked us to be nice to that Steve bloke.

Sonia Why should she do that?

Clinton	We'd had a go at him in the Changing room.
	The boys can hardly talk for laughing and Clinton punches Stuart on the arm.
Stuart	We got him to wash my socks.
Andy	We tied them round his mouth and shoved him under the tap. It was a right mess. Water everywhere.
Stuart	Shame Kingston had to come in and spoil all the fun. I will say this for Steve, though, he didn't grass us up.
Natalie	(*shocked*) That was rotten and cruel!
Sonia	It wasn't very nice of you.
Gordon	He didn't mind. He told Kingston it was a joke.
Clinton	And then, Mrs Powers only goes and has a quiet word with us. She asked us to be nicer to him. Help him settle in and all that.
Louise	Why did you have to pick on him? He's done you no harm.
Stuart	If he tells the world he's going to be a bodyguard, he gets what's coming to him.
Louise	(*angrily*) He didn't tell the world. He told me, and I was stupid enough to tell you.
Stuart	You should learn to keep your mouth shut, then.
Louise	How was I supposed to know you'd have a go at him?
Stuart	It was a joke, okay?
Louise	You think you're so hard just because you hang around with Neil Fisher.
Sonia	You want to watch out, Stuart, it'll only get you into trouble.
Stuart	Mind your own business!
Louise	Don't have a go at her! I was the one who started all this. You're right, I should have kept my mouth shut.
	Louise leaps to her feet in distress and starts to leave the room.

Natalie Now look what you've done! Come on, Sonia, let's go after her.

The girls leave the room.

Clinton Women!

Stuart Yeah, they can never see the joke.

Scene Six

Characters: Louise, Steve.

Later, the same day. In the Registration room. Steve is alone. Louise enters the room.

Louise I've been looking everywhere for you. Where have you been hiding?

Steve What's it to you?

Louise (*embarrassed*) Look, I think I owe you an apology.

Steve What for?

Louise You know, that business in the Changing room. If I had kept my big mouth shut, they wouldn't have picked on you.

Steve (*shrugging*) It doesn't matter.

Louise You don't make it easy for anybody to be friends with you.

Steve I don't want friends.

Louise Everyone needs friends.

Steve Friends let you down. Anyway, there's nobody in this dump worth knowing.

Louise That's because you haven't tried to get to know anybody.

Steve It's easy for you, you've been here since Year Seven, and you're a girl. I've never fitted in anywhere.

Louise (*angrily*) Don't talk to me about fitting in! Take a look around. How many black kids do you see? Don't tell *me* about being different.

Steve You're paranoid. I haven't been here that long, but I haven't noticed people treating you differently.

Louise That's because I work hard at fitting in. It'll pay off in the end, you'll see. I intend to get all the qualifications I can, make something of myself, get a career in business. Not like you and all this stupid bodyguard stuff.

Steve I'm not bothered about this place. I know I don't exactly have the right image for a bodyguard, but I'm working on it, I've joined a gym.

Louise That sounds expensive.

Steve My mum pays. She feels guilty now I've moved in with Gran. She'll pay for anything, just to clear her conscience.

Louise I didn't know you lived with your Gran.

Steve It's peaceful there, not like at home, with that git, Graham, going on at me all the time.

Louise Who's Graham?

Steve My mum's boyfriend.

Louise My mum hasn't got time for boyfriends, she's too busy working.

Steve What does she do?

Louise She works for a firm of solicitors, on the admin side. She wants to be a proper solicitor, so she studies for her exams, morning, noon and night. There's just me and her at home. I'm an only child.

Steve So am I.

Louise My mum expects me to be just like her, only better.

Steve My mum couldn't care less. All she cares about is Graham. You're lucky.

Louise   It doesn't feel that way sometimes. You should try living up to my mum's expectations!

Steve   Try living down to *my* mum's!

They laugh.

Louise   Do you want to come round to my house after school?

Steve   Okay.

Louise   I'll see you later, outside the front gates.

Steve   Yeah, later.

They smile at each other shyly and Louise leaves the room.

Scene Seven

Characters: Mary, Angie, Steve, Louise.

A few days later. In the kitchen at Steve's Gran's house. Mary, Steve's Gran, is sitting at the table, drinking a cup of tea. Angie, Steve's mother, enters.

Mary   Where have you been hiding yourself?

Angie   That's a nice greeting, I must say. Aren't you even going to offer me a cup of tea?

Mary   I've just made a fresh pot. Get another mug.

Angie gets a mug, returns to the table and sits down. There is an awkward silence as they drink their tea.

Angie   So, how are you?

Mary   Why should you care? You hardly ever come to see us.

Angie   (*sighing*) Oh, Mum.

Mary   Steven may as well not exist for all you care.

Angie   That's not fair! It's not my fault he doesn't get on

	with Graham. They never stopped arguing. I tried to make it work, I really did.
Mary	It would help if you saw him more often, took an interest in his life.
Angie	Oh, Mum.
	They hear the noise of the front door opening.
Mary	Is that you, Steven?
	Steve calls from the hall.
Steve	Yes, Gran. Louise's with me.
Angie	Who's Louise? Has he got a girlfriend?
Mary	Ssh! Don't go on at him.
	Steve and Louise enter the room. When he sees his mother, Steve's grin changes to a scowl.
Angie	Hello, Stevie, got a kiss for me?
	She offers her cheek, which Steve ignores.
Angie	Aren't you going to introduce me to your girlfriend?
Steve	She's not my girlfriend, she's Louise. You've got a one-track mind.
Angie	How was I supposed to know? I haven't seen you for ages.
Mary	Now, you two, stop arguing. What's Louise going to think of us? Cup of tea, Louise?
Louise	No thanks, Mrs Richards. I just stopped off to get a book for homework.
Steve	It's in the front room. Come through and I'll find it for you.
Louise	It was nice meeting you, Mrs err . . .
Steve	Come on, Louise, I'll find that book.
	Steve leaves the room quickly. Louise gives a small embarrassed smile and follows him.
Angie	Well, well, our Stevie with a girlfriend.
Mary	Will you just drop it! She's not his girlfriend. How many more times?

There is an awkward silence. Angie looks at her watch.

Angie   Is that the time? I'd better be going. I'll try and pop round in a week or so. You can always phone me if there's anything urgent. 'Bye, Mum.

Mary   'Bye. Let yourself out.

Angie leaves the room. Mary remains seated at the table.

Scene Eight

Characters: Steve, Louise.
A few minutes later. In the front room.

Steve   So, now you've met Angie, the mum from hell.

Louise   She's not that bad.

Steve   You don't know her. It really winds me up, the way she calls me Stevie.

Louise   Why does she call you that?

Steve   It's what she called me when I was little, Angie and Stevie. It makes me want to puke. And when that Graham moved in . . .

Steve picks up a cushion, punches it hard and throws it back down on to the settee. Louise smoothes the cushion and sits down on the settee.

Louise   It must have been awful.

Steve   Yeah, well. They'll see. He won't be able to push me around for much longer. I'm getting fit! You wait and see, nobody will be able to mess with me.

Louise   I can't stop long. Have you got the Geography book I lent you?

Steve   It's here somewhere.

         *Steve crosses the room and takes a book from a pile
         on a chair, hands it to Louise and sits down next to
         her.*

Steve   Thanks for letting me borrow it.

Louise   That's okay.

         There is an awkward pause.

Louise   So, you're getting fit. How's it going at the gym?

Steve   (*enthusiastically*) Great! I go most nights and at
         weekends.

Louise   Isn't that rather a lot?

Steve   You should come with me, I'll show you how to use
         all the machines and that.

Louise   I don't think it's my scene.

Steve   You should see some of the blokes, you wouldn't
         believe some of the weights they can lift. I can't
         wait to be the same as them.

         Louise looks at him.

Louise   Actually, you do look different.

Steve   You'll notice an even bigger difference soon, I'm
         getting some pills to hurry my programme along a
         bit.

Louise   (*alarmed*) Do you think that's a good idea? You're
         fine as you are.

Steve   Do you think so?

Louise   There could be side-effects.

Steve   Don't worry, I'll just take the vitamin pills, I wouldn't
         touch the other sort. Especially now I know it would
         upset you.

Louise   Well, you're a mate.

         Steve moves closer.

Steve   Is that all I am? Can't I be something more?

Louise   Steve, I'm sorry but . . .

Steve puts his arm around Louise and tries to kiss her.

Steve   Come on, Louise, I've liked you for ages.

Louise   No!

Louise pushes him off and leaps to her feet.

Steve   I thought you really liked me.

Louise   I do, but not in that way.

Steve   But we spend a lot of time together.

Louise   I felt sorry about Stuart and that lot picking on you.

Steve   So you tried being nice to me. Well, I don't need anybody being nice to me!

Louise   I do like you, honest, but not as a boyfriend. I want to get my exams and then go to college. I haven't got time for boyfriends.

Steve   Just like your mum.

Louise   What's my mum got to do with it?

Steve   You told me she doesn't have time for boyfriends. You're just like her.

Louise   I think I'd better go.

Steve   Why don't you just say it? You're ashamed for anyone to think you might want to go out with me.

Louise   No! It's just that . . . I'm really sorry, honest.

Steve   You're just like all the rest. But you'll see, I'll show all of you. When I'm famous you'll all want to know me and I'll laugh in your faces!

Louise   I've got to go. I'll see you at school tomorrow.

Steve   Not if I see you first.

Louise leaves the room. Steve slumps back into the settee.

Scene Nine

Characters: Natalie, Sonia, Louise.

The next day. In Sonia's bedroom. Sonia is sorting through the clothes in her wardrobe and Natalie is looking through a stack of CDs.

Natalie	What are you going to wear?
Sonia	I don't know, something comfy, I expect.
Natalie	I feel nervous, everybody checking out what I look like out of school uniform.
Sonia	It's only the school disco.

Sonia adds a skirt to the pile of clothes on the floor. She pauses, suddenly realising.

Sonia	Of course! It's Gordon, isn't it? You fancy him!
Natalie	(*embarrassed*) Don't be stupid! I just want to look my best, that's all.
Sonia	Gordon won't notice anyway. You'd have to wear football boots to make him notice.

The girls giggle.

Sonia	Actually, he's not bad.
Natalie	Who?
Sonia	Gordon. Stop pretending you don't fancy him, you could do worse. Just look at how Louise's got herself involved with Steve.
Natalie	I think she fancies him.
Sonia	Yeah, she's always hanging around with him. She hasn't got time for us these days.

Natalie puts a CD on at full volume. The girls dance around the room to the music. They do not hear a loud banging at the door. It is Louise. She opens the door and enters the room. Natalie and Sonia are surprised to see her. Natalie turns down the volume.

Louise	Hi, I thought I'd pop round for a chat and catch up on things.
Natalie	Oh, you've got a few minutes to spare for us, have you?
Louise	What's that supposed to mean?
Natalie	Don't pretend you don't know! Sonia was just saying how you're always hanging around with that new boy these days.
Sonia	It's all right, Louise, you can tell us.
Louise	Tell you what?
Natalie	About how you fancy him. Everybody's talking about it.
Louise	But I don't, that's the trouble! Oh, what have I done?
	Louise sits down on the bed. She is almost in tears.
Natalie	What are you going on about?
Louise	Even my best friends think I fancy him. It's all my fault!
	Louise bursts into tears. Natalie sits down next to her.
Sonia	What's wrong?
Louise	It was awful! I didn't mean to lead him on, I feel so ashamed!
	Sonia and Natalie look at each other in alarm.
Natalie	Sonia, turn the music off!
	Sonia rushes across the room and turns off the music. She grabs a tissue, rushes back to Loiuse and hands it to her.
Sonia	What's happened? Tell us!
Louise	Promise you won't tell anyone?
Natalie	Of course we won't, we're your friends.
Louise	Steve came on to me when I was round at his house.

Natalie   (*shocked*) What?

Sonia   Oh, Louise! What happened? Did he . . .?

Louise   (*interrupting*) Nothing happened! He tried to kiss me and I wouldn't let him.

Sonia   Is that all?

Natalie   (*angrily*) It's enough! Don't be so stupid, Sonia, you can see she's upset.

Sonia   Sorry.

Louise   It's okay. If anyone's stupid, it's me.

Natalie   What do you mean?

Louise   Steve really thought I fancied him.

Natalie   It did look that way. You were spending more and more time with him.

Louise   I didn't fancy him, honest. If I hadn't told Stuart and that lot about Steve wanting to be a bodyguard, they wouldn't have picked on him. I thought I could make it up to him by trying to be his friend.

Sonia   Sorry for thinking you fancied him, but that's what everybody thought.

Louise   (*smiling*) I did overdo it a bit. Even his mum thought I was his girlfriend!

Natalie   He introduced you to his mother? It must be serious.

The girls laugh.

Louise   She was there when I went round to his Gran's house.

Natalie   Only joking!

Louise   What am I going to say to him at school tomorrow?

Natalie   Nothing. Just pretend that it never happened and we'll make sure you're not left on your own so that he can't speak to you about it, won't we, Sonia?

Sonia   Yes, I'll stay with you all the time, Louise.

Louise Thanks. I don't think he will try to speak to me though. It's just that I'm embarrassed at even being in the same room as him.

Sonia Don't worry, it'll be okay. We'll look after you.

The girls smile at each other.

Scene Ten

Characters: Sonia, Stuart, Clinton, Andy, Gordon, Steve.

The next day at morning break. In the Registration room. The room is empty except for Stuart, Gordon, Andy and Clinton, who are arguing about football. Sonia rushes in.

Sonia Have you seen Louise anywhere?

Stuart Why should I want to see her?

Clinton looks under the table.

Clinton No, she's not here.

The boys laugh.

Gordon What do you want her for anyway?

Sonia I've lost her and I'm supposed to be looking after her. Natalie will kill me if she finds out.

Andy Why?

Sonia It's private and you wouldn't understand in any case.

Stuart You're not a very good guard if you've lost her already. Break's only just started.

Sonia (*miserably*) I know. We were just leaving the Science Block and one minute she's behind me and the next minute she's gone. What am I going to do?

Stuart   If I were you, I'd ask Steve to give you a few lessons.

Sonia   No, not him! I don't want to talk to him!

Clinton   I expect that's who Louise is with.

Andy   Who?

Clinton   Steve. She really fancies him.

Sonia   No she doesn't!

Stuart   Yes she does! Even Gordon's noticed!

Gordon   Noticed what?

Sonia   It's all a big mistake. She . . . oh, never mind.

Stuart   Here's Steve now. You can ask him yourself.

Steve enters the room.

Sonia   *Please* don't say anything!

Stuart ignores her.

Stuart   We were just talking about you, Steve. We were saying how Louise really fancies you.

Sonia   It's not true!

Stuart   How do you know?

Sonia   She told me! Oh, I really hate you!

Stuart   It looks like you're out of luck, Steve.

Steve   What?

Stuart   Go on, admit it. You and Louise fancy each other.

Gordon   Leave him alone.

Steve   I don't know what you're talking about.

Stuart   Then I'm going to have to remind you.

Stuart moves towards Steve menacingly and Steve backs away.

Sonia   No! Gordon, stop him!

Gordon moves quickly to stand between them.

Gordon   That's enough. The joke's over. Haven't you got somewhere else to go, Steve?

Steve   Yeah, right.

Steve moves towards the door.

Stuart	We're not just going to let him go, lads, are we?
	Andy and Clinton look away uncomfortably.
Stuart	Andy?
Andy	Gordon's right. Let him go.
Stuart	Clinton?
Clinton	It's nearly the end of break anyway.
Stuart	You lot are no fun at all. Never mind, I'll speak to you later, Steve. All right?
	Steve does not answer. He leaves the room and the others watch him go.

Scene Eleven

Characters: Mrs Powers, Louise, Natalie, Sonia.

Several weeks later at lunchtime. In the Registration room. Mrs Powers is sitting at her desk. Louise, Natalie and Sonia enter.

Mrs Powers	Louise, I don't suppose you've seen anything of Steven Richards?
Louise	No, why?
Mrs Powers	He's not been in school for quite a while. You're a good friend of his, you might know something.
Louise	No, Mrs Powers, I haven't seen him at all.
Mrs Powers	If you do happen to hear anything, perhaps you could let me know. I think I shall have to alert the authorities over this one. Goodness, is that the time? I should have been at a meeting five minutes ago.
	Mrs Powers leaves the room in a hurry. Louise, Natalie and Sonia sit down.

Louise   I don't know why Mrs Powers asked me about him.
          I haven't seen him for ages.

Natalie That's because he hasn't been at school for ages.

Sonia   Oh, no!

Natalie What's the matter with you?

Sonia   I don't think Steve's been to school since Stuart
          tried to have another go at him.

Louise   (*surprised*) What? When was this? Why didn't you
          tell me?

Sonia   I didn't think it was important. Nothing happened.
          Gordon stopped him.

Louise   Stopped who?

Natalie What's this about Gordon?

Louise   Shut up, Natalie. Tell me everything, Sonia.

Sonia   Well, remember that day I was supposed to be
          looking after you and I lost you?

          Louise nods impatiently.

Sonia   Stuart was teasing me about you fancying Steve . . .

Natalie (*interrupting*) You didn't say anything about what
          happened between him and Louise?

Sonia   No, I didn't! He just seemed to guess that something
          was going on. You know what he's like.

Louise   It's all my fault again. If only I'd kept my big mouth
          shut.

Sonia   Well, Steve came in and Stuart started on him.
          I really thought he was going to hit him. Gordon
          stopped him.

Natalie (*sarcastically*) And you didn't think it was important.

Sonia   (*miserably*) I didn't tell you because I didn't want to
          get the blame for Stuart thinking Louise and Steve
          fancied each other. How was I to know he'd stop
          coming to school?

Louise   It's all my fault. I'll have to do something before

Mrs Powers sends the authorities in.

Natalie   Why don't you phone him?

Louise   It's not as simple as that, I need to talk to him properly. I'm worried about what he may have got up to.

Sonia   What like?

Louise   He said he was going to get some pills to make his muscles bigger. He might be getting them at the gym.

Natalie   Wow! He wouldn't be so stupid, would he?

Louise   I don't know, that's the trouble. When he thought I'd be his girlfriend he told me he'd only take vitamin pills. He seemed really pleased that I cared. But now . . .

Natalie   Taking that stuff is dangerous, somebody should talk to him.

Louise   I know that, but he doesn't know anybody, except me.

Louise stands up and starts to pack her bag, ready for afternoon school.

Natalie   Why don't you go round to his house after school?

Louise   His Gran would get suspicious. She might think he's still coming to school.

Sonia   I know, go to the gym, and see if he's there. You can go after school one day.

Louise   I could do, but the gym's in a dead rough neighbourhood and I'd be nervous about being there at night.

Natalie   How about if we came with you?

Natalie and Sonia stand up and pick up their bags.

Louise   No. He'd never listen to me if I had you two in tow. I've got to try to see him during the daytime and I'll have to go soon. I could skip PE this afternoon. Nobody would miss me, we only play table tennis.

Natalie	If anybody asks, we'll say you're at the toilet.
Louise	Thanks.

The girls leave the room.

Scene Twelve

Characters: Mr Freeman, Louise.
The next morning. In Mr Freeman's office. Louise knocks at the door.

Mr Freeman	Ah, Louise, come in and take a seat. I think you know what this is about, don't you?
Louise	Sir?
Mr Freeman	It's a small matter of not being present in PE yesterday afternoon.
Louise	Sir?
Mr Freeman	Come along, Louise, don't play games with me.
Louise	I'm not playing games. I don't know what you mean.
Mr Freeman	You excused yourself, without permission, from PE yesterday afternoon.
Louise	I didn't, Sir, I was there all afternoon.
Mr Freeman	No, Louise. When Miss Wright took the register, you were not there.
Louise	I must have been in the toilet, Sir.
Mr Freeman	No, you weren't. Miss Wright noticed you were missing and asked your friends where you were. They said you were at the toilet and so she decided to keep an eye out for you. The funny thing was, she didn't see you all afternoon. I don't think you were at the toilet all afternoon, do you?

Louise does not answer.

Mr Freeman I'm waiting, Louise. What do you have to say for yourself?

Louise Nothing, Sir.

Mr Freeman Did you truant yesterday afternoon?

Louise Yes, Sir.

Mr Freeman Would you like to tell me why?

Louise I can't.

Mr Freeman You're not helping yourself, you know. This is most unlike you. You must have had a very good reason. If my memory serves me right, you've hardly ever truanted before.

Louise (*indignantly*) I've *never* truanted before.

Mr Freeman There we are then. So tell me about yesterday.

Louise looks uncomfortable.

Louise It's Steve Richards, Sir.

Mr Freeman The new boy?

Louise Yes.

Mr Freeman Go on.

Louise I'm worried that he hasn't been in school for a while so I went to look for him.

Mr Freeman Are you a special friend of his?

Louise No! Why does everbody think that? I'm just worried about him. I think he might be taking stuff that isn't good for him.

Mr Freeman (*alarmed*) Drugs! Do you mean drugs? Has he brought them into school?

Louise It's not what you think. He's into bodybuilding and I think he's taking those pills that make you stronger.

Mr Freeman Do you mean anabolic steroids?

Louise I don't know what they're called, I just had to talk to him about it, so I went to the gym he goes to, that's all.

Mr Freeman Why do you think he'll listen to you?

Louise It's a long story and it's partly my fault he's not coming to school. I wanted to put things right, sort it all out for him.

Mr Freeman And you decided to sort it all out in school time?

Louise I had to see Steve as soon as possible. I overheard Mrs Powers say that she was going to call in the authorities about him being absent.

Mr Freeman Quite right too. You can't take matters into your own hands, you know. Where would we be if everyone did as they wished?

Louise loses her temper.

Louise All I was trying to do was help a mate out! Is that such a crime?

Mr Freeman I'd prefer it if you didn't speak to me in that tone of voice, young lady!

Louise It's all right for us to take care of each other when it suits you and your school image. It's another thing when we try to help a mate who's in trouble.

Mr Freeman (*sharply*) That will do! Who do you think you are, talking to me like this?

Louise (*standing up*) I've had it with this place. I'm going!

Mr Freeman If you walk out now, I'll have to take the matter further.

Louise doesn't answer and leaves the room.

Scene Thirteen

Characters: Louise, Tina.

Later the same day. At Louise's house. Louise is sitting in the kitchen. Tina, Louise's mother, enters the room.

Tina   What's going on? Mr Freeman phoned me at work to say you truanted yesterday, and that when he tried to speak to you about it this morning, you were very rude to him. Not only that, you'd walked out of school and he didn't know where you were.

Louise   Seems like you know all there is to know.

Tina   Hey, this is your mother you're talking to! I think you should put me in the picture.

Louise   A boy called Steve has stopped coming to school. He'd been bullied. I think he's taking bodybuilding pills and he works out all the time, so I went to look for him at the gym he goes to. I hoped to try and talk some sense into him.

Tina   I've told you before that you can't take the whole world on your shoulders.

Louise   It's *my* fault, Mum! I feel responsible.

Tina   Why?

Tina sits down next to Louise. Louise tells her all about Steve, the bullying, and the misunderstanding.

Tina   You've got to put yourself first. You can't take responsibility for how Steve behaves.

Louise   Don't *you* start, I've had enough from Mr Freeman!

Tina   So was Steve at the gym?

Louise   No. It was horrible, really rough, I felt scared.

Tina   I thought you said he worked out all the time.

Louise   That's what he told me.

Tina   Telling and doing are two different things. He
            sounds like a real loser.

Louise Okay, I got it wrong but at least I tried.

Tina   And now you're going to try to put things right at
            school.

Louise I'm not going back, Mum.

Tina   And I say you are! You're my daughter and you're
            not going to hide away and ruin your own future
            just because things didn't work out the way you
            planned. We've got an interview with Mr Freeman
            tomorrow morning and we'll both be there.

Louise But Mum, I can't. I don't know what to say to him.

Tina   You'll start by apologising. I want him to see you've
            been raised properly, with manners and respect for
            your elders. You look exhausted. Go and take a bath
            and I'll get you something to eat.

Louise Yes, Mum.

            Louise starts to leave the room.

Louise Mum?

Tina   What now?

Louise Do you think I was wrong to try to find Steve and
            talk to him?

Tina   Everybody does what they've got to do, that's all
            there is to it. And when you get yourself into a hole,
            you've got to get yourself out again.

Louise (*smiling*) You crack me up! Where do you get all
            your sayings from?

Tina   From your Grandma. Now go and run that bath,
            child, then you can tell me the whole story from
            start to finish.

Louise Everything?

Tina   (*firmly*) Everything.

            *Louise leaves the room. Tina sits down in the chair
            and sighs to herself.*

Tina   Kids, who'd have them?

Scene Fourteen

Characters: Mr Freeman, Louise, Tina.
Early on Monday morning, before school. In Mr
Freeman's office.

Mr Freeman Thank you for coming in so early, Mrs Webster.

Tina It's important that Louise can get back to lessons quickly.

Mr Freeman That does rather depend upon her attitude.

Tina She's got the right attitude. She's here to apologise, aren't you, Louise?

Louise (*muttering*) Yes.

Tina Louder, girl!

Mr Freeman I'm sure that Louise is sorry for the way she behaved.

Tina She is. I've brought her up properly, she knows better.

Mr Freeman Quite. What about you, Louise? What do you have to say for yourself?

Louise I'm sorry I truanted and I'm sorry I was rude to you.

Mr Freeman You should know better than to take matters into your own hands. It only makes matters worse.

Tina Hold on a minute. Louise has apologised for truanting and speaking out of turn, but I think she was quite right to try to help her friend. She just went about it in the wrong way.

Louise (*embarrassed*) Mum!

Mr Freeman I don't quite follow.

Tina Everybody's got to do what they've got to do if they see a wrong and want to make it right. She told me what happened, and her careless talk made trouble for him. She felt responsible and wanted to help. Quite honestly, Mr Freeman, I hope she goes on helping. I'm proud of her.

Mr Freeman Well there's no doubt that her heart's in the right place, perhaps she's a little misguided in her approach. Let's put all this business behind us and get on with the job of making sure you get good grades in your examinations.

Louise I do have my own opinions, you know!

Mr Freeman I had noticed.

They all laugh.

Tina Is there any news about Steve?

Mr Freeman The Truancy Officer made an emergency visit, and when she got there, his Gran was out but Steve was in. It seems that instead of coming to school, he'd been hanging around the shopping centre, going back to his Gran's when he was sure she was out.

Louise Then all that stuff about going to the gym wasn't true.

Mr Freeman He had been going on and off but not regularly.

Louise Somehow, I don't think he'll get to be a bodyguard.

Mr Freeman Neither do I. It's like these lads who can play the guitar a bit and think they'll become pop stars.

Tina Some people do get to realise their ambitions. The thing is, you have to be determined and have a lot of luck along the way, if you're going to turn your dreams into reality.

Louise Don't mind her, Sir. She's full of this sort of advice. She gets it from my Grandma.

Tina Louise!

Louise Mum!

They all laugh.

The End

Natalie

List of Characters

Year Nine pupils
Natalie
Louise
Sonia
Stuart
Clinton
Gordon
Andy
Rosemary
Ella

Year Eleven pupils
Nigel, Rosemary's brother
Omar, Nigel's friend and a disc jockey

Teachers
Mr Kingston, French/PE
Miss Wright, Food Technology

Other pupils
Lighting Crew 1 (LC 1)
Lighting Crew 2 (LC 2)
Lighting Crew 3 (LC 3)
Audience 1–6

NATALIE

Scene One

Characters: Natalie, Sonia, Louise.

A Saturday in June. In Sonia's bedroom. Sonia is sorting through the clothes in her wardrobe. Natalie is looking through a stack of CDs.

Natalie What are you going to wear?

Sonia Nothing special, it's only the school disco.

Natalie It's all right for you, you never care much about what you look like.

Sonia That's not true!

Louise enters the room.

Louise Hi! Your mum said to come up, Sonia.

Natalie You've been ages. You were supposed to be here an hour ago.

Louise I had to go to the library, my books were overdue.

Natalie Meet anybody interesting?

Louise (*smiling*) No one *you'd* call interesting.

Natalie What's that supposed to mean?

Sonia (*giggling*) Boys! She means boys. You know, your hobby.

Natalie That's not true!

Sonia Just getting my own back on you for saying I don't care what I look like.

Natalie Well, you don't.

Sonia At least I don't worry all the time about what I'm going to wear, what I'm going to eat, who's going to see me, what they'll think of me.

Natalie	What's wrong with wanting to look nice and wear the latest fashion?
Louise	Nothing. And you always do look really nice.
Sonia	Yes, you seem to know what goes with what. I wish I did.
Natalie	(*gloomily*) It doesn't seem to get me anywhere. I still can't get a boyfriend.
	Louise and Sonia laugh.
Louise	See what I mean? There's more to life than boys, you know.
Natalie	(*sulkily*) Go on, turn it all into a big joke.
Sonia	Why don't you ask Gordon to go to the disco with you?
Louise	Gordon! Do you fancy Gordon?
Sonia	Haven't you noticed? That's why we have to hang around in the Registration room at lunchtimes, just in case Gordon puts in an appearance.
Louise	Actually he's not bad, if you like talking about football all the time.
Natalie	I can't ask him to the disco, he has to ask me.
Sonia	It's cool for girls to ask guys out these days.
Natalie	Not this girl. I'd die of shame if he said no.
Louise	You'll just have to hope that he's there and that he notices you.
Natalie	Exactly! I've got to make an impression. So what am I going to wear?
	Sonia and Louise groan.
Sonia	I'll help you choose. You can borrow anything from my wardrobe, even the dry-cleaning bags.
Natalie	Very funny.
Louise	And I'll try to find out if Gordon is going to the disco. It's no good going to all this trouble if he's not even going to be there.

Sonia   There might be someone else there for her.

Natalie   You're making me out to be a right flirt! How will you find out if Gordon will be there? I don't want the whole world to know that I fancy him.

Louise   I'll ask Rosemary Lomax, she knows everything. Her older brother plays football with Gordon, so she's bound to know.

Sonia   Put some music on, Natalie, it'll help us concentrate on what you're going to wear.

Natalie puts on a CD. She turns the volume up and the girls turn their attention to the clothes.

Scene Two

Characters: Stuart, Andy, Clinton, Gordon, Natalie, Sonia, Louise, Rosemary, Ella.

A few days later at lunchtime. In the Registration room. Pupils are sitting in groups at tables, chatting amongst themselves.

Stuart   Disco, disco, that's all we ever hear about these days.

Andy   Are we going to it?

Stuart   You can, I'm not. It'll be really boring.

Clinton   I've heard that the lighting crew lads have come up with some good special effects.

Andy   Omar in Year 11 is the DJ. He's got loads of mixer decks and some cool music.

Gordon   Sounds too technical for me. I'd rather watch *Match of the Day*.

Stuart   Same here.

Clinton   I'm going, it'll be a laugh.

Andy	(*to Stuart*) It won't be the same without you and Gordon. Go on, come. It'll be a right laugh.
Clinton	When things get boring, we can do a few chants.
Gordon	(*grinning*) Now you're talking.

Ella and Rosemary are talking at another table.

Ella	Just listen to that lot. How juvenile can you get?
Rosemary	(*ignoring her*) Well, this is what Hayley said this girl said to her.
Ella	What girl?
Rosemary	The girl that told Hayley.
Ella	Who's she?
Rosemary	Oh, shut up and listen to what I'm telling you!

At another table.

Natalie	I'm not sure it's a good idea to ask Rosemary. She's such a big mouth.
Sonia	Let's ask Stuart.

Before Natalie can stop her, Sonia calls across the room to Stuart.

Sonia	Stuart! Are you going to the disco?
Stuart	Not you as well. Can't anybody find anything else to talk about?
Rosemary	(*joining in*) Are you going, or not?
Clinton	We haven't made up our minds yet, have we lads?
Gordon	No, we haven't got a thing to wear.
Andy	We'll have to go naked.

The boys laugh.

Stuart	I expect *you're* all going.
Ella	We wouldn't miss it for anything, would we, Rose?

Rosemary nods enthusiastically.

Rosemary	Everybody will be there.
Stuart	I suppose you've got to go. I mean, just think of all the gossip you'd be missing.

Rosemary	I like to be informed, it shows an active mind. Not like some I could mention.
	The girls laugh.
Ella	You're quiet, Natalie. Are you okay?
Natalie	I'm fine. We don't all talk a mile a minute.
Rosemary	Are you going to the disco, Natalie?
Natalie	I don't know yet, it depends.
Rosemary	On what?
Sonia	Natalie is . . .
Louise	Sonia!
	Louise speaks to Rosemary.
Louise	We're still thinking about it. I expect we will, though.
	Rosemary shrugs her shoulders and calls to Stuart.
Rosemary	The music's going to be really good. Omar's doing it.
Clinton	Told you!
Stuart	All right, all right.
Ella	And there are going to be competitions.
Sonia	I didn't know that. What sort?
Ella	(*doubtfully*) I don't know about all of them, but I think there's going to be a quiz.
Gordon	Big deal.
Ella	And a Miss T Shirt competition.
Andy	What? What was that? Cor!
Louise	Did you say a *Miss* T Shirt competition?
Clinton	(*grinning*) Yeah, it might even get Stuart to go.
Louise	That's typical of you lot! Who are the teachers organising this thing?
Rosemary	Mr Kingston and Miss Wright.
Louise	I'm going to have words with them! I mean, it's one thing to have a T shirt competition. But a *Miss* T Shirt? No thank you!

Clinton   Spoilsport.

Natalie   You always have to get involved, Louise. Why can't you just leave things alone? I was thinking I might enter.

Louise   Natalie! How could you, where are your principles?

A bell rings.

Sonia   That was a quick lunch hour.

Rosemary   It always is. Why is it that the best bits of the day go the quickest and the rest is just a drag?

They all laugh and start to collect their things together for afternoon school.

Scene Three

Characters: Rosemary, Ella, Sonia.
The next day at school. On a corridor.

Ella   Look, there's Sonia.

Rosemary   She's on her own for a change. I thought something funny was going on yesterday, when Louise shut Sonia up. Let's see what we can find out.

Ella   (*admiringly*) You don't miss a thing. How do you do it?

Rosemary   I've got an active mind. Hey, Sonia, wait!

Sonia turns around.

Sonia   Oh, hi!

Rosemary   Natalie doesn't seem to be too happy these days.

Ella   She was really quiet, apart from when she had a go at Louise.

Sonia	She's got a lot on her mind at the moment.
Ella	Like what T shirt to wear for the competition!
Rosemary	That's if Louise will let her go in for it.
Sonia	(*indignantly*) Louise doesn't tell us what to do!
Rosemary	You've got to admit that she interferes a lot.
Sonia	(*smiling*) She can't help it. She told Natalie not to worry about going to the disco without a boy. She said lots of girls would be there on their own.
Ella	We aren't going with boys.
Sonia	Oh, you know Natalie. She has to wear the right clothes, do the right thing and she really wants a boyfriend.
Rosemary	Does she? Anyone in particular, or isn't she fussy?
	Rosemary and Ella laugh. Sonia looks uncomfortable.
Sonia	You know what I mean.
Rosemary	Does she fancy Stuart? She was looking across at his table all the time yesterday.
Sonia	No way! She likes Gordon.
Rosemary	Does she?
Sonia	Oh, no, I wasn't supposed to tell! She'll kill me if she finds out!
Rosemary	Don't worry, we won't say anything, will we, Ella?
Ella	No, we won't tell a soul.
	Rosemary changes the subject.
Rosemary	Anyway, are you all going to the disco?
Sonia	(*relieved*) I hope so.
	She pauses in thought.
Sonia	Is Gordon going?
Rosemary	Don't know.
Sonia	Could your brother find out?
Rosemary	That's an idea. I'll ask him and let you know.

Sonia	Thanks. You won't tell him it's me that wants to know, will you?
Rosemary	No.
Sonia	And you won't say anything about Gordon?
Ella	Your secret's safe with us.
Rosemary	We'd better get a move on, we're late already. See you, Sonia.
Sonia	See you.

Rosemary and Ella watch as Sonia walks off quickly along the corridor.

Rosemary	That was easy.
Ella	What are you going to do now?
Rosemary	Don't know yet. Sonia is really dumb. You were brilliant, *'your secret's safe with us'*!

Rosemary and Ella burst into fits of laughter.

Scene Four

Characters: Rosemary, Ella, Nigel, Omar.

Later the same day. At Rosemary's house. Rosemary, Ella, Nigel, Rosemary's brother in Year Eleven, and his friend Omar are sitting around drinking tea and eating biscuits.

Ella helps herself to another biscuit.

Ella	These are nice, all chocolatey.
Nigel	Save some for the rest of us.
Omar	I thought you girls didn't eat biscuits. Got to look after your figures and all that.

Rosemary	Don't believe everything you read in that teeny magazine your sister buys.
Omar	(*offended*) I don't read that stuff.
Nigel	Yes, you do. You were reading it when I knocked for you the other day.
Ella	Natalie Harvey counts every calorie.
Nigel	Stupid.
Rosemary	She thinks that if she's thin, it will help her get a boyfriend.
Omar	What?
Rosemary	A boyfriend, she really wants one.
Omar	If she was my sister, I'd give her a right talking to.
Rosemary	I see, one rule for you and one rule for the rest of us. What about the Miss T Shirt competition that you two are organising for the disco?
Omar	That's different, it'll be a laugh.
Ella	And is your sister going to enter?
Omar	No way!
	Rosemary and Ella exchange scornful looks.
Nigel	It's nothing, just a bit of harmless fun.
Omar	It'll help sell tickets and the more money, the better. After all, it's all in a good cause.
Rosemary	What cause?
Omar	The school swimming pool.
Ella	Big deal! We'll have left by the time they get round to even starting to build it.
Nigel	Where's your community spirit?
Ella	*You* dress up in a tight T shirt and parade about, then!
Nigel	No girl has got to take part if she doesn't want to.
Rosemary	It doesn't bother me but you'd better watch out for Louise Webster. She's really annoyed about it.

Nigel	That's all I need.
Omar	(*laughing*) I'm really scared.
Ella	If anyone can change your plans, Louise can.
Rosemary	How did you get it past the committee? I can't see Miss Wright agreeing and Kingston does anything she tells him.
Nigel	They weren't at the final disco meeting, so by the time they find out it'll be too late.
Rosemary	Then there'll be plenty of boys there for Natalie to choose from, though she seems to have set her heart on Gordon.
Nigel	(*in disbelief*) Who? Did I hear you right?
	Nigel and Omar burst out laughing.
Ella	Sonia told us.
Omar	Gordon's not interested in girls! He only likes football.
Rosemary	Don't let on it was us who told you.
Nigel	Would I, Sis? What do you take me for?
Ella	Can I have that last biscuit?
Rosemary	Ella!
Ella	I can't help it if I'm hungry.
Omar	I'll split it with you.
	Omar breaks the biscuit in half, shares it with Ella and they all discuss the disco music.

Scene Five

Characters: Stuart, Clinton, Nigel, Omar.
The next day. On the way to school.

Stuart How's it going?

Nigel Not bad, not bad.

Omar We're pretty busy, as it goes. There's a lot to get ready for the disco.

Clinton From what I've heard, it's going to be really good. Good lighting effects, great music and Miss T Shirt.

Nigel If Louise has her way, the competition's off. She's trying to get it cancelled.

Stuart My mate Neil won't be happy. He's only going for the competition.

Omar I don't know why you hang around with him, he's bad news.

Stuart He's a good mate. You don't know him like I do.

Omar (*shrugging*) Suit yourself.

Stuart I can take care of myself. Anyway, I hear that Natalie is going in for this competition.

Nigel Talking of Natalie. A little bird tells me she fancies Gordon.

Clinton What? Do me a favour!

Omar It's a right joke, you'd better warn him.

Stuart We will, mate, we will.

Clinton Keep us informed about the competition.

Nigel We will, mate, we will.

Omar Got to go, things to do. Catch ya' later.

Stuart Yeah, later.

Nigel and Omar hurry off. Stuart and Clinton walk slowly. Stuart is deep in thought.

Scene Six

Characters: Stuart, Clinton.
A few minutes later.

Clinton   I can't wait to see Gordon's face when we tell him about Natalie.

Stuart   Why tell him?

Clinton   What?

Stuart   We could have a bit of a laugh out of this.

Clinton   How?

Stuart   Natalie fancies Gordon, right? Only he doesn't know and he'd never notice anyway.

Clinton   Right.

Stuart   So we won't tell him, we'll give him a little hint to help things along a bit.

Clinton   How?

Stuart   We write him a letter and make out it's from Natalie, all about how she fancies him and is looking forward to seeing him at the disco and all that.

Clinton   But why write a letter?

Stuart   'Cos we write another one to somebody else saying the same thing and then we stand back and wait for it all to happen.

Clinton   I don't get it.

Stuart   That's because you're thick. I'll tell you again. Two letters, one to Gordon and one to another bloke, both letters from Natalie, both letters saying the same thing, about how she fancies him and will meet him at the disco.

Clinton   How will they know they're from Natalie?

Stuart	We'll write them on the computer and forge her signature. I'm quite good at forgery.
Clinton	Gordon'll never fall for it.
Stuart	Yes, he will, 'cos he's that stupid. He only knows about football.
Clinton	Who will the second letter be to?
Stuart	Andy.

Clinton laughs in disbelief.

Clinton	Andy! He hasn't got a clue about anything, he doesn't even know what day it is half the time.
Stuart	Exactly! Neither of them knows anything about women, that's why they'll fall for it. I'll meet you in the Computer Room after school.
Clinton	(*grinning*) You crack me up!
Stuart	I can't help it if I'm a genius. I'll see you later.

The boys go their separate ways.

Scene Seven

Characters: Louise, Miss Wright, Mr Kingston, Nigel, Omar.

A few days before the disco. On a corridor outside the Library. Miss Wright and Louise are deep in conversation.

| **Miss Wright** | I'm very puzzled. I can assure you that I knew nothing about Miss T Shirt until you drew my attention to it and I feel exactly the same as you, it's an appalling idea. |
| **Louise** | I didn't think you would have anything to do with it, |

Miss, but I heard that it's all official and that it's been passed by the Disco Committee.

Miss Wright That must have been the one I missed. Come to think of it, I never saw the minutes either. Ah, here's Mr Kingston, perhaps he knows about it.

Mr Kingston joins them.

Miss Wright Louise was just telling me about the Miss T Shirt competition.

Mr Kingston The what?

Miss Wright Apparently there are plans afoot to hold a Miss T Shirt competition at the disco and Louise and her friends quite rightly think that it's most inappropriate.

Louise You should hear all the boys going on about it. They've all bought tickets.

Mr Kingston (*smiling*) Yes, I can see how it might be a crowd puller.

Miss Wright I beg your pardon?

Mr Kingston Sorry.

Miss Wright I was telling Louise that it must have been passed at the last committee meeting.

Mr Kingston I don't know, I wasn't there. I had a football practice.

Miss Wright You might have told me. I wasn't at the meeting either.

Louise I was wondering if you could change it into something for everyone so it'll be just a T shirt competition.

Miss Wright I think that's a good idea.

Mr Kingston It won't attract as much attention.

Miss Wright Really!

Mr Kingston Sorry. Nigel and Omar must have been behind this. It beats me how they thought they would get away with it.

Miss Wright	They very nearly did. If it hadn't been for Louise, we wouldn't have known. We'll use her idea and make it unisex.
Mr Kingston	Yes, of course, but I don't know how much take-up from the boys you'll get.
Louise	Thanks.
	Nigel and Omar come out of the Library.
Mr Kingston	Speak of the devil, or devils, I should say.
Omar	Oh, no, trouble!
Nigel	Quick, hide!
	Omar and Nigel start to walk off quickly in the opposite direction.
Miss Wright	Just a minute, boys. We would like a word with you.
	Omar mutters to Nigel.
Omar	And you can guess what about.
	He speaks to Louise.
Omar	Hi, Louise, fancy seeing you here.

Scene Eight

Characters: Stuart, Gordon.
Later the same day. In the Registration room.
Gordon is alone. Stuart enters.

Stuart	Have you heard the latest? Louise has managed to get that competition changed from Miss T Shirt to T Shirt. Nigel and Omar are well gutted.
Gordon	Mmm.
Stuart	What's up? Have you been dropped from the team?

Gordon   No.

Stuart   Then there's nothing to worry about, is there?

Gordon doesn't answer. Stuart goes over to Gordon and sits down next to him.

Stuart   Something's up.

Gordon still doesn't answer.

Stuart   Why don't you, me, Clinton and Andy go in for the competition? We can wear wigs and T shirts and shove balloons up the front and you can wear your football boots.

Gordon   We'll look stupid.

Stuart   It'll be a laugh. If that stupid Louise can spoil our fun, we can spoil her competition.

Gordon   I don't know if I'm going.

Stuart   Why? You were dead keen the other day.

Gordon   Well . . .

Stuart   You don't have to dance or anything, you can just watch.

Gordon   It's not that.

Stuart   So what's the problem?

Gordon   Promise you won't tell anybody?

Stuart   Would I? Remember me? I'm your mate.

Gordon   I've had a letter, it came this morning.

Stuart   So?

Gordon hesitates.

Stuart   Are you going to tell me, then?

Gordon   It's from Natalie. She wants to meet me at the disco, for a date.

Stuart puts on an expression of shocked surprise.

Stuart   Blimey! What's it say?

Gordon   You can read it if you want.

Gordon hands the letter to Stuart, who examines it with great interest.

Gordon   I don't know what to do.

Stuart   One thing at a time. Let me read it first.

Stuart reads aloud.

Stuart   *Dear Gordon, I hope you don't think this is too pushy of me but I didn't know what else to do so I thought I'd write you a letter. The thing is, I've liked you for quite a long time.* You're well in there, mate!

Gordon   If all you're going to do is wind me up . . .

Gordon tries to take the letter away from Stuart, who moves it out of his reach.

Stuart   Sorry, I'll be serious. Now, where was I? . . . *for quite a long time now, you know, not just as a friend, and I think that the way you look at me sometimes must mean you feel the same way about me.* I didn't know you fancied her.

Gordon   I don't. Well, I don't think I do.

Stuart continues to read.

Stuart   *There's always so many people around, your mates and my mates. I thought that the disco would be a good place for us to meet without the others suspecting –* she uses big words as well – *it's a date type thing.* A date! She's asking you out on a date! *I knew you wouldn't get round to asking me out.*

Gordon   She's right there.

Stuart   *So I thought I'd ask you. I can't think of what else to put, so I'll sign off for now and hope to see you at the disco, Natalie.*

Stuart gives the letter back to Gordon.

Stuart   Your luck really has changed!

Gordon   I don't know what to do.

Stuart   You fancy her, don't you?

Gordon   I don't know.

Stuart   She's a good-looking girl.

Gordon   Do you think so?

Stuart I do.

Gordon I've never been on a date before.

Stuart There's a first time for everything.

Gordon I'm not sure I want a girlfriend. I haven't got time, what with football practice and everything.

Stuart Well, it's up to you, but if you're asking me, girls like Natalie don't come along every day of the week.

Gordon I won't know what to say to her.

Stuart You don't have to say anything, just ask her to dance. Oh, I forgot, you can't dance. I know, buy her a Coke instead. You'll be too busy drinking to talk much.

Gordon (*doubtfully*) I don't know.

Stuart Tell you what. I'll come with you when you first kick off. I'll hang around till you've got warmed up and once you've got into your stride, I'll go and sit on the benches.

Gordon (*relieved*) Will you? Thanks.

Stuart That's what mates are for.

Stuart stands up and pats Gordon on the shoulder, reassuringly.

Gordon You won't tell Andy and Clinton about the letter, will you?

Stuart No worries.

Scene Nine

Characters: Natalie, Sonia, Louise.
The night before the disco. In Sonia's bedroom.
Natalie is wearing a short red dress.

Natalie Are you sure it looks all right? You're not just saying it?

Louise (*sighing*) For the millionth time, yes.

Sonia I think it looks better on me.

Louise and Sonia smile at each other. Natalie sits
down on the bed, angrily.

Natalie That's it! I'm not wearing this dress and I'm not
going to the disco.

Sonia We're only kidding. It looks great.

Natalie Are you sure?

Louise Here we go again. Leave off, Nat.

Natalie I want to make the right impression.

Sonia Don't worry, you will, especially in the T Shirt
competition.

Natalie I'm not going in for it any more. Why did you have
to poke your nose in?

Louise Because there are principles at stake. I don't
understand how you could go in for such a thing,
parading around in the spotlight with all those boys
whistling at you.

Natalie You're just jealous.

Louise (*incredulously*) Ha!

Sonia It's only a bit of fun and it'll be nicer now Louise has
made it for boys as well as girls.

Natalie (*gloomily*) It means not so many people will come
to the disco.

Louise	Boys, you mean boys.
Natalie	(*shouting*) All right, boys! What's wrong with that?
Sonia	(*anxiously*) Calm down, please!
Louise	I didn't realise it was such a big deal, sorry.
Natalie	(*calmer now*) I was really hoping that Gordon would be there. He won't go if Stuart doesn't go and Stuart won't go now the competition's changed.
Sonia	Gordon is going, they're all going. Rosemary Lomax told me.
Louise	How does she know?
Sonia	Stuart told her brother and her brother told her.
Louise	I'm glad that's settled. Now we can all relax.
Sonia	I can't wait. Do you think Miss Wright and Mr Kingston will dance together?
Natalie	I expect so, they're not ancient, you know.
Louise	She really put him in his place about the competition. He wasn't against it at all!
Natalie	There you go, not everyone is as narrow-minded as you.
Sonia	I wish it was tomorrow.
Louise	Oh, yes! *'When I look into Gordon's eyes my life will change for ever.'*
Sonia	Don't mind her, Natalie, she doesn't understand about these things.

Louise collapses on to the bed in laughter.

Scene Ten

Characters: Stuart, Andy.

The morning of the disco. Before school, in the playground. Stuart is reading a letter. Andy is impatiently waiting for him to finish.

Stuart *So I thought I'd ask you. I can't think of what else to put, so I'll sign off for now and hope to see you at the disco, Natalie.*

Andy (*excitedly*) What do you think?

Stuart (*admiringly*) I'd say you're well in there.

Andy Do you think so?

Stuart I'll say!

Andy Do you think she fancies me? I mean, she must do to write me this letter.

Stuart Grab the chance while you can. Girls like Natalie don't come along every day of the week.

Andy She sounds like a right goer, a right bird. No bird's ever fancied me before

Stuart Let me give you a word of advice, don't call her 'bird'.

Andy (*puzzled*) Why not?

Stuart Take it from me, they don't like it.

Andy (*shrugging*) If you say so. I can't wait.

He pauses.

Andy I've just remembered, I can't dance. She won't want me to dance, will she?

Stuart Nah, all the girls dance together these days.

Andy (*relieved*) That's all right then.

Stuart Are you still on for the T Shirt competition?

Andy   (*enthusiastically*) Yeah! I haven't got a wig but that don't matter. I've borrowed some of my mum's make-up. I'll put that on instead.

Stuart   Clinton's bringing the balloons.

Andy   It'll be a right laugh.

Stuart   (*smiling*) You can say that again.

Stuart and Andy walk into school.

Scene Eleven

Characters: Omar, Nigel, Rosemary, Ella, Lighting Crew 1 (LC 1), Lighting Crew 2 (LC 2), Lighting Crew 3 (LC 3).

The night of the disco. In the School Hall. Pupils are standing around. Omar has set up his disco equipment on the stage and is busy testing it. All the lights are still on. Nigel is standing at the back of the Hall. Rosemary and Ella are standing near the front.

Omar speaks into the microphone.

Omar   Can you hear me at the back?

Nigel   Yes, that's good, Omar.

Omar speaks into the microphone again.

Omar   I'll try some music. By the way, sorry for the delay, folks. There've been a few technical hitches.

Omar turns off the microphone and calls across to the lighting crew, who are frantically working on the lighting board, at the side of the stage.

Omar   Hurry up, you lot. I can't get everybody going with all these lights on.

LC 1 It's not our fault, we weren't allowed in here till an hour ago.

LC 2 It was Gym Club and they made us help put all their stuff away.

Omar Can't you be quicker?

LC 3 Tell him to shut up! I'm going as fast as I can.

Omar speaks into the microphone.

Omar Won't be long now, folks, we'll soon be ready to rock and roll. Just to get things started, you might remember this one.

Just as Omar is about to put on some music, the lights suddenly dim. Everyone cheers. Just as suddenly, the lights come up again. Everyone groans.

Omar Slight hitch, folks. There's nothing wrong with the music, though. So let's get started!

Loud music fills the Hall.

Rosemary This is useless.

Ella We might have known.

Nigel joins Rosemary and Ella.

Rosemary What a waste of time this has turned out to be.

Nigel Stop moaning, it's only just started. It'll be better when there are some more people.

Ella No one's dancing.

Nigel It's still early.

Rosemary It would help if it was darker. So much for the special effects.

Nigel Give them a chance! I've got to check up on the refreshments. See you later.

Nigel rushes off. Rosemary scans the Hall. She sees Natalie, Louise and Sonia. Natalie is wearing the red dress and is nervously trying to pull it to make it longer.

Rosemary What does Natalie think she looks like? That dress couldn't be much shorter.

Ella I think she looks nice. You're in a mood because your plans for stirring it between her and Gordon haven't come off.

Rosemary I haven't had a chance, have I? Every time I've tried to get either of them on their own, to drop a few hints, their mates have turned up.

The lights dim again and the special effects spotlights start to pulse. Everyone cheers.

Scene Twelve

Characters: Natalie, Sonia, Louise, Stuart, Clinton, Omar, Miss Wright, Mr Kingston.

At the disco. A few moments later.

Louise That's a bit better, now the lighting's fixed. Let's dance.

Sonia Oh no, Louise, I couldn't.

Natalie Besides, no one else is.

Louise Somebody's got to be first.

Sonia (*pointing*) Look over there! It's Gordon and he's on his own.

Natalie Don't point, it will make him look at us.

Sonia (*puzzled*) I thought that's what you wanted.

Louise It's okay, he's not coming across.

Natalie Let's dance.

Sonia You didn't want to a minute ago.

Natalie Well, I do now.

Sonia	But that will make him look at you more.
Louise	That's the whole point.
Sonia	I don't get it.

Natalie and Louise lead the way on to the dance floor. Sonia trails behind.

Clinton and Stuart enter the Hall. They avoid Gordon and make their way to the back.

Clinton	He can't keep his eyes off her.
Stuart	All the same, I think he's going to need a bit of help.
Clinton	Not like Andy. From what you've told me, we'll have to tie him down!
Stuart	It should be good. Where is he, anyway?
Clinton	He went to put all our gear in the changing room, ready for the competition.
Stuart	He's a good lad, he's got his uses.
Clinton	I thought Neil was coming.
Stuart	He was, until they changed the rules for the competition. Anyway, this isn't his scene, there's no booze. Come on, let's get things moving with Gordon.

Stuart and Clinton walk over to Gordon. Miss Wright and Mr Kingston are standing near the entrance to the Hall.

Mr Kingston	It all seems to be going quite well.
Miss Wright	Now they've sorted out the lighting.

There is a pause in the music. Omar speaks into the microphone.

Omar	It's me again, folks, the man with the plan and the plan is to get you all dancing.

Miss Wright and Mr Kingston raise their voices as the music blares out.

Mr Kingston	Young Omar has certainly got what it takes. He's doing a great job.

Miss Wright If you like this sort of music. I do think it's a bit loud. Perhaps you could have a word with Omar, and at the same time could you find out what time the competition is due to start. We'll need to get a member of staff backstage and more of us here on the floor to keep order.

Mr Kingston Expecting riots, are you?

Miss Wright Better safe than sorry.

Mr Kingston I'll go and find out. Fancy a dance later?

Miss Wright Maybe, but not to this rubbish.

Mr Kingston I'll ask Omar to put on something more suitable, a nice slow one perhaps.

Miss Wright I don't think so!

Mr Kingston Only joking.

Mr Kingston leaves the Hall. Miss Wright continues to watch the dancers.

Scene Thirteen

Characters: Stuart, Clinton, Gordon, Andy, Natalie, Louise, Sonia.

A few minutes later. Stuart and Clinton join Gordon on the edge of the dance floor.

Clinton See anybody you fancy?

Gordon What makes you say that?

Clinton No reason, I just wondered.

Stuart There's Louise and her mates. Let's go and say hello.

Gordon hesitates. Stuart pushes him forward.

He speaks to him in a low voice.

Stuart You've got to get the ball rolling. I'll be right behind you.

Gordon, Clinton and Stuart move across to join Natalie, Louise and Sonia. Stuart positions himself behind Gordon so that he can give him instructions without being overheard by the others.

Clinton We saw you dancing.

Louise Some of us can.

Stuart digs Gordon in the ribs.

Stuart (*to Gordon*) Go on, kick off!

Gordon (*nervously*) Hi, Natalie.

Natalie Oh hi, Gordon.

There is an awkward pause.

Gordon You look nice in that dress.

Stuart (*to Gordon*) Excellent pass! Now keep the ball in play.

Natalie Thanks.

Sonia It's my dress, actually. I let her borrow it.

Louise Sonia!

Sonia What?

Louise Shall we go and get a Coke?

Sonia I'm not thirsty.

Stuart (*to Gordon*) Don't let Sonia's tackle put you off.

Gordon I was just thinking of getting a Coke. Do you want one, Natalie? I'll pay.

Stuart (*to Gordon*) Nice recovery.

Natalie Yes, all right.

Stuart (*to Gordon*) Ask her to go with you.

Gordon Do you want to come with me?

Before Natalie can answer, Andy rushes up. He winks at Stuart and pushes Natalie on the arm,

*almost making her lose her balance. She clings on
to Gordon for support and he holds her arm to
steady her.*

Natalie   Oi!

Andy   Watcha', Nat. Pleased to see me, are you?

*Stuart is beginning to enjoy himself. Clinton is trying
hard not to laugh.*

Stuart   Offside!

Louise   What did you say?

Natalie   What's going on?

Andy   Why are you and Gordon holding on to each other?

Natalie and Gordon move apart hastily.

Stuart   Corner!

Sonia   What are you on about?

Stuart   In the corner, Miss Wright, see, she's watching us.

Louise   I'm not surprised with all the pushing and shoving
that's going on.

Andy   I thought you'd be pleased to see me, Natalie,
especially after you know what . . .

Stuart   Penalty shoot out!

Omar's voice comes across the PA system.

Omar   It's the moment you've been waiting for, folks, it's
competition time! All the contestants meet up with
Mr Kingston backstage. And get a move on! We've
got a lot to get through on this action-packed night
of rockin' rhythm!

Stuart   That's us. Come on, lads, let's get ready.

Gordon   Are you entering, Natalie?

Natalie   No, I've changed my mind.

Louise   Bet you're glad you did now!

Clinton   Sure we can't make you change your mind back
again?

Natalie	Positive.
Gordon	I'll see you later.
Natalie	Yes.

Gordon and Natalie smile shyly at each other.

Andy	I'll see you later as well, Natalie. I'll give you a wave from the stage.

Andy leans forward and whispers in Natalie's ear.

Andy	(*whispering*) I know you're my number one fan.

Natalie pushes him away.

Natalie	Get off!

*Andy shrugs his shoulders and grins at Natalie.
Stuart and Clinton are trying hard not to laugh and
the boys go off to get ready for the competition.
Andy takes Stuart to one side.*

Andy	Are you sure she fancies me?
Stuart	Yeah, no worries, she's playing hard to get, that's all.
Andy	I expect you're right, I'll wave to her from the stage.
Stuart	You do that.

*Stuart and Clinton hold on to each other in helpless
laughter.*

Gordon	What's the joke?
Clinton	Nothing, mate, nothing.

Scene Fourteen

Characters: Natalie, Sonia, Louise, Rosemary, Ella.
A few minutes later. Rosemary and Ella join Natalie, Sonia and Louise at the edge of the dance floor.

Rosemary	What was all that about?
Sonia	What do you mean?
Rosemary	There seemed to be quite a party going on.
Ella	I thought Natalie was going to push Andy over!
Louise	Nothing's going on. Why do you always have to know everything?
Rosemary	(*offended*) Suit yourself. I like the dress, Natalie.
Sonia	It's mine.
Ella	Gordon seemed to like it as well.
Natalie	What's that supposed to mean?
Rosemary	Everybody knows you fancy him.
Natalie	I do not!
Rosemary	Just trying to be friendly, we know when we're not wanted. Let's go, Ella.

Rosemary and Ella start to walk away. Natalie calls after them.

Natalie	Go and spy on somebody else!

Rosemary stops and gives Natalie a look full of dislike, then she continues to walk away.

Sonia	I think you've upset them.
Natalie	So?
Sonia	I wouldn't like Rosemary Lomax for my enemy.
Louise	Forget it, she's all mouth. You were getting on well with Gordon though, until Andy butted in.
Sonia	Yes, what was all that about?

Natalie   I don't know. He went on about me being his
              number one fan.

              Louise and Sonia laugh.

Natalie   Exactly! I'm not that desperate.

Louise   Oh Nat, you're great! I hope it works out for you
              with Gordon.

              They turn their attention to the stage.

Scene Fifteen

*Characters: Stuart, Clinton, Gordon, Andy, Omar, Mr
Kingston, Lighting Crews 1–3, Audience 1–6.*

*The competition is about to start. Omar puts on
some music and joins Mr Kingston backstage.*

Omar   Where is everyone?

Mr Kingston You tell me. I've sent Nigel out front to see who he
                 can round up.

Omar   Hang on, who's this lot coming?

                 *Stuart, Clinton, Gordon and Andy arrive. All are
                 wearing wigs, except for Andy, whose face is heavily
                 made up. All are wearing short skirts, football boots,
                 socks and T shirts with balloons shoved up the
                 front. Omar and Mr Kingston burst out laughing. The
                 lighting crew come to see what's going on.*

LC 1   What *do* they look like?

LC 2   I wouldn't have the nerve.

LC 3   It's pathetic, is this all there is? Some competition
                 this has turned out to be.

LC 1   Looks like the lights will be the best bit of this disco.

Omar	And the music.
LC 2	Yeah, well, it's not bad.

The lighting crew go back to work.

Andy	This mascara stuff is making my eyes stick together.
Mr Kingston	Let's get on with it, announce them, Omar.
Omar	Right!

Omar runs back on to the stage, stops the music and speaks into the microphone.

Omar It's competition time, folks! Not quite what we expected, I have to say, we've only got four contestants.

There are jeers and cries of disbelief from the audience.

Omar But I'm sure you'll agree that they'll more than make up for the rest. So put your hands together for Stuart, Clinton, Gordon and Andy!

Gordon	Are we the only ones?
Clinton	It looks like it.
Gordon	I'm not going on then. I feel a right fool.
Stuart	Yes, you are.

Stuart pushes Gordon forward on to the stage and follows him. Clinton follows and Andy trails behind. Andy peers into the audience, sees Natalie and gives her a big wave.

Andy (*shouting*) Natalie! Hi, Natalie!

He speaks to Clinton.

Andy Why doesn't she wave back? I thought she fancied me.

Clinton She does, she's just shy. Give her another wave.

Andy waves again. There are howls of laughter and jeers from the audience.

Audience 1 Is this it?

Audience 2 Get 'em off!

Audience 3 Show us your legs, Andy.

Audience 4 Do a little twirl, Clinton.

Audience 5 Hey, Stuart, you've got a ladder in your tights!

Audience 6 Put the music back on, Omar, this is boring.

Mr Kingston signals to the lighting crew to dim the stage lights and mimes to Omar to put some music on. Gordon scowls at Stuart.

Gordon You and your stupid ideas!

Stuart and Clinton collapse in laughter. Andy looks forlornly on as Gordon angrily leaves the stage.

Scene Sixteen

Characters: Rosemary, Ella.

A few minutes later. At the edge of the dance floor. The music is still playing. Ella rushes over to Rosemary.

Ella Look what I found on the floor in the corridor. It's addressed to Andy.

Ella holds out an envelope. Rosemary takes it from her and examines it.

Rosemary He must have dropped it. We'll give it back to him . . . after we've read it.

Rosemary takes out the letter and they quickly read it together, peering in the dim light. When they have finished reading, they smile at each other.

Ella I thought it was Gordon she fancied.

Rosemary So did I.

Ella   Sonia knew all along it was Andy that Natalie
              fancied. She was trying to put us off.

Rosemary (*thoughtfully*) Mmm.

Scene Seventeen

*Characters: Natalie, Louise, Sonia, Rosemary, Ella,
Stuart, Clinton, Gordon, Andy.*

*In another part of the Hall. Pupils are dancing in
groups to the music. Rosemary and Ella join Natalie,
Louise and Sonia.*

Rosemary I just wanted to say sorry, Natalie.

              *Natalie, Louise and Sonia look at Rosemary in
              surprise.*

Louise   Am I hearing right?

Rosemary I shouldn't have said you fancied Gordon.

Ella   That's what Sonia told us.

Natalie   Sonia!

Sonia   I didn't mean to, honest, it just slipped out.

Natalie   I thought you were my friend!

Sonia   I am!

Rosemary She is. It was very clever of her to make us think it
              was Gordon you fancied, when all along it was
              Andy.

Natalie   What? Do me a favour!

Ella   Why else would you write him this letter, then?

Natalie   What letter? What are you going on about?

Rosemary This letter! Ella found it in the corridor.

Louise   Let me see.

Louise takes the letter and starts to read it. She pauses and looks up at Natalie.

Louise   Did you really write this? Oh, Natalie, how could you be so stupid?

Natalie   I haven't written anything.

Natalie snatches the letter from Louise and reads it quickly.

Natalie   I didn't write this!

Rosemary You must have, you signed it. Even Louise thinks you wrote it.

Natalie   That's not my signature!

Stuart, Clinton, Gordon and Andy arrive. They have changed out of their costumes. Andy still has make-up on his face. He tries to put his arm round Natalie, who pushes him away.

Andy   I thought you liked me.

Natalie   Well I don't, and I don't know where you got that idea from!

Andy   But you must, you wrote me a letter.

Rosemary Told you! Ella found your letter, Andy, you must have dropped it.

Andy   I thought I'd lost it. See, Natalie, you must like me, you wrote me a letter.

Natalie   I never did!

Stuart and Clinton exchange glances.

Gordon   (*interrupting*) Natalie can't fancy you, she fancies me. You wrote me a letter, didn't you, Natalie?

Natalie   (*angrily*) No! I didn't write any letter!

Gordon   But I've got it here. It's all about how you like me and want to meet me at the disco.

He takes a letter from his pocket.

Gordon	That's why I offered to buy you a Coke.
Andy	That's what my letter says.
Natalie	(*angrily*) For the last time, I didn't write any letters to anybody!
Louise	Give me both letters.

Natalie and Gordon give the letters to Louise and she tries her best to examine them in the dim light.

Louise	As far as I can make out, they're both the same, almost word for word, and this is definitely not Natalie's signature.
Natalie	Told you!
Rosemary	Let me see.

Rosemary reaches out for the letters but Natalie snatches them from Louise.

Natalie	You're not going to see them!
Ella	But if you didn't write them, what have you got to hide?
Natalie	(*furiously*) Shut up!

There is a silence whilst Natalie carefully examines the letters.

Natalie	These are a forgery. Look! They have been done on a computer. The only handwriting is the signature and that's definitely not mine. I'll prove it if you don't believe me. Who's got a pen?

Louise suddenly notices Stuart and Clinton. They are holding on to each other, trying not to laugh.

Louise	You two! I might have known it!
Stuart	Don't look at me. I don't know anything about any letter.
Gordon	Yes, you do! I showed you mine.
Andy	So did I!
Louise	You're nothing but trouble, Stuart Davis!
Rosemary	That's right, you tell him!

Louise	(*to Rosemary*) Keep out of this, you've caused enough trouble!
Rosemary	Sorry I spoke.
Andy	It wasn't you, was it, Stuart? You wouldn't do this to a mate.
Natalie	Oh, yes he would! He'd do anything for a laugh.
Louise	Yes, and stupid Clinton will do anything he says.
Clinton	Oi! Who are you calling stupid?
Sonia	Was it you, Stuart?
Stuart	I don't know why everybody's so upset. It was only a bit of fun.
Gordon	I've had enough of you. You're always winding me up, making me out to be a fool.
Rosemary	That's right, you tell him, Gordon!
Natalie	Don't you speak to Gordon like that!
Stuart	The trouble with you, Gordon, is that you can't take a joke!
Gordon	Come over here and say that! I've had enough of you!
	Gordon moves threateningly towards Stuart, who starts to back away. Natalie holds Gordon back.
Natalie	No, don't! He's not worth it!
Rosemary	Oh, so she does fancy him after all!
Natalie	What did you say? Let me at her!
	Natalie lets go of Gordon and lunges at Rosemary. Gordon tries to grab Stuart. At the same moment the Hall is plunged into darkness and the music grinds to a halt. There is a lot of shouting and jeering.
Sonia	What's happened?
Ella	I think the lights have failed.
Louise	So much for the special effects!
Stuart	Let's get out of here!
Clinton	I'm right with you, mate!

Stuart and Clinton quickly leave. The house lights suddenly come back on and everyone blinks at the sudden glare. Gordon looks round for Stuart.

Gordon Where is he?

Sonia He's gone, and so has Clinton.

Louise That's typical.

Andy Does that mean you don't fancy me, Nat?

Natalie That's right, Andy, I definitely don't fancy you.

Andy Suit yourself.

Andy walks off slowly.

Gordon Sorry, Natalie.

Natalie It wasn't your fault.

Gordon You shouldn't have held me back, though. You should have let me punch him when I had the chance.

Natalie And get yourself suspended?

Gordon Why should you care?

Natalie I don't. I just don't think he's worth it. Why do you stay friends with him, anyway? He's always causing trouble.

Gordon He's not my friend after tonight. Andy can do what he likes but I'm not going to hang around with him any more.

Meanwhile, Omar has managed to get the music going again.

Omar Sorry about the technical hitch, folks, but everything is up and running again now, so let's see you out there on the floor.

Louise Come on, Sonia, let's dance, that's what discos are for.

Louise grabs Sonia's arm and drags her on to the dance floor.

Sonia (*grumbling*) All right, don't be in such a rush.

*Louise and Sonia go off to dance. Gordon shuffles
his feet. There is an awkward pause.*

Gordon   I do think you look nice, though, in that dress.

Natalie   (*embarrassed*) Thanks.

Gordon   Do you still want a Coke?

Natalie   Okay.

*Natalie and Gordon walk off towards the
refreshment area.*

The End

Andy

List of Characters

Year Nine pupils
Andy
Stuart
Clinton
Gordon
Louise
Natalie
Sonia

Teachers
Mr Kingston, French/PE
Miss Wright, Food Technology
Mrs Powers, Form Tutor
Mr Freeman, Deputy Head

Members of Chefs' Club
Richard
Tony
Jamie

Year Eleven pupils
Neil, Stuart's friend
Year Eleven Pupil 1
Year Eleven Pupil 2
Year Eleven Pupil 3

Year Seven Pupils
Kevin, Andy's brother
Paul, Kevin's friend

Others
Ms Roberts, MP
School Secretary (School Sec.)

ANDY

Scene One

Characters: Andy, Miss Wright.
At the end of morning school. In the Food Technology room. Miss Wright is folding tea towels. Andy is wiping round the sink area.

Miss Wright Thanks for staying behind and helping to clear up.

Andy That's okay, Miss. It wasn't a lot.

Miss Wright You seem to enjoy cooking. Have you thought about catering as a career?

Andy I'm not very good at the writing part.

Miss Wright You need to get some practical experience. That will go a long way towards making up for your weakness on the theory side.

Andy Do you think so?

Miss Wright You should think about coming back to Chefs' Club. Why did you stop attending?

Andy It's on at the same time as football practice.

Miss Wright I'm not trying to pressure you, but if you want to take up catering as a career, you're going to have to be serious about it, and that might mean giving up football. Think about it at least.

Andy All right.

Miss Wright (*smiling*) It's Chefs' Club next week, so maybe I'll see you there. Thanks again for all your help.

Andy Yes, Miss. Thanks, Miss.

Andy starts to leave the room. Miss Wright calls him back. She picks up a large plastic container.

Miss Wright	Don't forget your bread rolls.
	Andy takes the container.
Andy	Thanks, Miss. I'd forgotten all about them.
	Andy leaves the room. Miss Wright smiles and watches him go.

Scene Two

Characters: Andy, Stuart, Gordon, Louise, Natalie, Sonia.

Five minutes later. In the Registration room. Louise, Sonia, Natalie and Gordon are chatting. Andy and Stuart enter. Andy puts his box of bread rolls on a table. Stuart opens the box.

Stuart	Let's have a look.
	He stuffs a roll into his mouth.
Stuart	These are tasty, just like the frozen ones my mum gets.
Natalie	You're disgusting, talking with your mouth full.
Stuart	Don't look then. Anyway, I'm in a rush. I've got to meet Neil behind the Science Block. I'll have another roll for later.
	Stuart grabs a roll and the box falls off the table. He rushes out of the room.
Louise	Why do you put up with him?
Andy	He's my mate.
Sonia	But he's so horrible to you.
Andy	Not all the time. He's a laugh!
Gordon	I've gone right off him, especially now he's hanging

round with Neil Fisher in Year Eleven. They think
they're well hard.

Natalie Don't you still do football practice with him?

Gordon That's different. I'm not going to give up my football
just because of him.

*Sonia picks up the box of rolls and hands them to
Andy.*

Sonia Only two fell on the floor, I've given them a wipe.
They do look nice, you are clever.

Andy You can have one if you like.

Sonia Are you sure? You haven't got many left.

Andy You can all have one.

They divide the rolls and start to eat them.

Natalie These are really good. You should be a chef.

Andy (*pleased*) That's what Miss Wright said. She wants
me to go back to Chefs' Club but I can't.

Louise Why not?

Andy It's football at the same time.

Gordon I'd go to Chefs' Club if I were you. It's not as if
you're that good at football.

Natalie Gordon!

Andy He's right, I'm useless at it. I only go 'cos Stuart likes
me to go with him.

Natalie You don't have to do everything that Stuart says.

Andy We're mates.

Louise If Stuart wanted to do something, he'd just do it. He
wouldn't think about you.

Andy Miss Wright said going to Chefs' Club would help
me get a job in catering.

Louise Do it then!

Sonia Chefs can make a lot of money these days.

Gordon Yeah, and when I'm a famous footballer, I can visit
you in your famous caff.

They all laugh.

Louise   You should think of yourself, Andy. Join Chefs' Club.

Andy   I think I will.

Natalie   I'm glad that's settled. Can I have another roll?

Sonia   Me too.

Andy   I haven't got many left. Oh, go on then, I can always make some more tonight.

Andy hands round the box of rolls and they all help themselves.

Scene Three

Characters: Andy, Miss Wright, Richard, Tony, Jamie, Mr Kingston.

A few weeks later. In the Food Technology room at Chefs' Club. Miss Wright is talking to the group.

Miss Wright   There's going to be a meeting here at the school. The Headteachers of other schools, the Governors and our local MP will be attending. The Music and Drama departments will provide the entertainment and we have been asked to provide the buffet.

Richard   What sort of food will we have to make?

Miss Wright   Sandwiches, salads, chicken drumsticks, cold desserts, that sort of thing.

Tony   It sounds like a lot of work.

Miss Wright   It is, but I'm sure you're up to it. It's a marvellous opportunity for Chefs' Club to really shine.

Jamie   But there are only four of us.

Miss Wright	That's why it will take a lot of careful organising and planning. I've decided to ask Andy to take charge.
Andy	(*astonished*) Me?
Richard	Him?
Tony	He can't organise anything!
Miss Wright	(*firmly*) Yes, he can. I have every confidence in you, Andy.
Andy	I'm not sure, Miss . . .
Miss Wright	(*interrupting*) Nonsense! It's your big opportunity and I'll be here to give you all the support and advice you need.
Andy	(*doubtfully*) Well, if you think so.
Miss Wright	Good. You should all go and get some lunch now.

Richard, Tony and Jamie leave the room. Andy packs his bag. Mr Kingston enters.

Mr Kingston	Ah, Andy. So this is where you've been hiding yourself. Why haven't you been to football practice? We've missed you.
Andy	I go to Chefs' Club now, Sir.
Miss Wright	(*smiling*) Andy's my star pupil. He's going to organise the buffet for the Head's meeting.
Mr Kingston	Is that so?
Andy	Yes, Sir. Miss Wright thinks I'm up to it.
Mr Kingston	Good luck to you.
Andy	Thanks. I'm going for my lunch now, Miss.
Miss Wright	Yes, fine, I'll arrange a time for us to meet later to talk over the details.

Andy leaves the room.

Scene Four

Characters: Miss Wright, Mr Kingston.
A few moments later. In the Food Technology room.

Mr Kingston	Are you sure this is a good idea? Don't you think you're giving the boy too much responsibility?
Miss Wright	I think I can be the judge of that.
Mr Kingston	He's not too fast on the uptake. It might all be too much for him.
Miss Wright	He's very keen to study catering and I think he should be encouraged.
Mr Kingston	Perhaps Andy isn't as talented as you think.
Miss Wright	You don't know anything about catering. I know what it is, you're annoyed that Andy has stopped going to football.
Mr Kingston	It's not that at all. Let's not quarrel.
Miss Wright	You started it.
Mr Kingston	Okay, okay, don't say I didn't warn you when it all goes wrong.
Miss Wright	Don't worry, I won't. And just for your information, nothing will go wrong. It will be a raging success.
	Miss Wright glares at Mr Kingston and he shrugs his shoulders.

Scene Five

Characters: Andy, Louise, Stuart.

Two weeks later. In the Registration room. Andy and Louise are reading through a pile of Andy's notes and lists.

Andy   I'm useless at this. I'm supposed to have these lists ready for Miss Wright by the end of the day.

Louise   I wish you'd told me earlier, that would have given us more time.

Andy   I didn't like to. I'm supposed to be in charge.

Louise   She'll never know I'm helping out. That's what friends are for. Now, where were we?

Andy hands Louise a pile of lists and they sort through them.

Louise   What about the puddings?

Andy   We're making as many as we can early and freezing them.

Louise   Good idea.

Andy   I've got to give Miss a list of how much stuff I think we'll need.

Louise   How much ham do you need?

Andy   I don't know, that's the trouble.

Louise   Don't worry, I'll get my calculator and we'll work it out.

Stuart enters the room.

Stuart   What's all this, then?

Andy   It's my lists for the buffet, Louise is helping me sort it all out.

Stuart   That's all you ever do these days. You're really boring.

Louise   Leave him alone, he's got a lot to think about.

Stuart   (*ignoring her*) Really boring.

Andy   There's a lot to do and there's only four of us.

Louise   What about on the day? Have you got enough people to serve?

Andy   (*groaning*) I hadn't thought about that. This is really doing my head in.

Louise   I'll serve, if you like, and I'm sure Natalie and Sonia will as well.

Stuart   Anything for free food.

Louise   (*ignoring him*) I'll have a word with them and let you know.

Andy   Thanks, Louise, you're helping me a lot.

Stuart   (*sarcastically*) 'Thanks, Louise.' Why didn't you ask me? We're supposed to be mates.

Andy   I didn't think you'd want to. You don't like cooking.

Stuart   I don't, but I would have done it for you. Anyway, I've got man's work to do. Neil wants me to be look-out for the card game he's organising.

Andy   Look out for what?

Stuart   Teachers, thicko! A lot of money can change hands.

Andy   You mean gambling?

Stuart   You catch on quick. Come to think of it, we could get a nice earner going. You supply the sandwiches and I'll sell 'em. We'll have to give Neil a cut, of course. It's only fair, seeing as it's his card game.

Louise   Andy!

Stuart   (*interrupting*) You mind your own business!

Stuart speaks to Andy.

Stuart   Well, what about it?

Andy   No, I don't think so.

Stuart   See, that proves how boring you've got. Suit yourself, it was only an idea.

Louise	A pretty stupid one, if you ask me.
Stuart	As it happens, I didn't. I'm off. I haven't got time for girls' stuff.

Stuart leaves the room.

Louise	You're better off without him, I keep telling you he's nothing but trouble.
Andy	He's all right. He can be a laugh.
Louise	Yes, all the way to the Head's office and suspension.
Andy	(*worried*) You won't tell on him, you know, about the card game? He might think it's me who grassed him up.
Louise	(*scornfully*) It's none of my business. And for your information, I never grass.

Scene Six

Characters: Stuart, Neil, Kevin, Paul.

A few days later. In the playground. Neil, Stuart's friend in Year Eleven, is strolling through the middle of a group of Year Seven pupils, who are playing a game with a tennis ball.

Stuart	Neil! Wait up!

As Stuart hurries to catch him up, he accidentally gets in the way of the ball.

Paul	Oi, mind where you're going!
Stuart	Watch it! Who do you think you're talking to?

Kevin picks up the ball and puts it in his pocket.

Kevin	He's talking to you, bum brain.
Stuart	I'll have you for that!

Kevin   Oh, yeah, you and who else's army?

Stuart lunges towards the pupils, who giggle and back off. Paul calls from a safe distance.

Paul   We're not scared of you.

Kevin   Stuart's all mouth, he doesn't know anything. You should hear him going on about football to my brother!

Neil hears the commotion, turns and walks back to greet Stuart. He comes up behind Kevin and grabs him roughly with one hand by the back of his blazer. Kevin is lifted off his feet.

Neil   (*laughing*) Need some help?

Stuart   Stupid kids!

Neil lowers Kevin back to the ground but doesn't loosen his grip.

Neil   What was that you were saying about my friend?

Kevin   (*frightened*) I didn't say anything.

Stuart   You've changed your tune, not such a big boy now, are you?

Neil   Shall I slap him for you?

Stuart   No, it's okay, I know him, he's Andy's little brother.

Neil   He's got no brains, just like his brother.

Neil and Stuart laugh. Kevin looks down at the ground and shuffles his feet.

Neil   What shall we do with him?

Stuart   I think we'll let him off with a warning this time. We'll have the ball, though. Hand it over.

Kevin   I haven't got it.

Stuart   Yes, you have, I saw you put it in your pocket.

Neil reaches into Kevin's blazer pocket with his free hand, takes out the ball and passes it to Stuart.

Neil   You'll have to be better behaved in the future or we'll have to teach you a lesson, and you wouldn't like that, would you?

Kevin doesn't reply. Neil gives him a shake.

Neil   Answer me when I speak to you. Say, *'No, I
           wouldn't like you to teach me a lesson, Neil.'*

Kevin No, I wouldn't like you to teach me a lesson.

Neil   Neil.

Kevin Neil.

Neil   That's better. Come on, Stuart, we've got better
           things to do than hang around here.

           *Neil releases his hold on Kevin and starts to walk
           away. Stuart follows. He throws the ball up into the
           air and catches it, calling back to Kevin as he does
           so.*

Stuart Yeah, watch it, or I'll get you next time!

           *Kevin watches them dejectedly. Paul runs across to
           join him.*

Paul   Are you okay?

Kevin I'll live. (*angrily*) I hate Stuart Davis, he can only act
           that big when Neil Fisher's around to back him up!

Paul   He pushes your brother about.

Kevin That's 'cos Andy lets him. He wouldn't push me
           around if I got him on his own.

Paul   He's at least two feet bigger than you.

Kevin So! I've got more brains than him. I bet they're
           going for a smoke. Let's follow them, we can hide
           round the corner and listen to what they're saying.

Paul   What if they catch us?

Kevin They won't. (*grinning*) Anyway, we can run faster.

           *Stuart and Neil walk towards the back of the
           Science Block. Kevin and Paul follow them.*

Scene Seven

Characters: Stuart, Neil, Kevin, Paul.

A few moments later. Stuart and Neil are leaning against the Science Block wall. Neil takes out a cigarette to share with Stuart. Kevin and Paul are hiding round the corner, within earshot of their conversation.

Neil   You should have let me slap him one. Never mind, next time.

Stuart   Yeah. I can't stop long, I've got football practice.

Neil   Miss it for once.

Stuart   I can't, the team's already short now that Andy is at Chefs' Club all the time.

Neil   Too much conscience, that's your trouble. Anyway, what's so important about Chefs' Club? I thought Andy really liked his football.

Stuart   Haven't you heard? There's going to be a meeting at the school, loads of important people. Andy's in charge of the catering.

Neil   Andy! Do me a favour!

Stuart   That's what I thought. Do you still want me to be look-out at the card game?

Neil   Yeah, you haven't told anybody have you?

Stuart   (*hesitating*) No. I was wondering. The card game's on the same day as the meeting.

Neil   That's a bit of luck, there won't be so many teachers nosing around on lunchtime patrol, they'll all be too busy.

Neil passes the cigarette to Stuart.

Stuart   If I could get hold of a load of the sandwiches Andy's making for his do, would you be interested?

	I thought it would be nice for the lads to have something to eat.
Neil	That's very kind of you, Stuart my old son, you're catching on quick. It might take their mind off losing and having to hand over all their money.
Stuart	Talking about money . . .
Neil	(*interrupting*) I can't pay you anything for being look-out.
Stuart	No, I was thinking about the sandwiches.
Neil	What about them?
Stuart	(*hesitating*) I was thinking maybe . . . *Neil deliberately misunderstands him.*
Neil	About what sort we'd like. You choose. The lads aren't fussy about free grub.
Stuart	Yeah.
Neil	Ten past one, Room Five.
Stuart	Okay. *Stuart passes the cigarette back to Neil.*
Neil	And don't forget the sandwiches.
Stuart	I won't. I've got to go to football practice now, I'm already late, Kingston will have a go at me. He hates me, he's looking for any excuse to drop me from the team.
Neil	I've got to go myself. I've got to see somebody about some money he owes me. *Neil stubs out the remains of the cigarette and the boys walk off in the direction of the main part of the school. Neither of them notices Kevin and Paul, who come out of hiding.*
Paul	A card game! What day is it on?
Kevin	Next Wednesday, the same day as Andy's meeting. He doesn't talk about anything else at home.
Paul	You'd better tell him that Stuart is planning on stealing his sandwiches.

Kevin   No. If I do that, Stuart will want to know how Andy
            found out about the game. Anyway, it's his fault if
            he's stupid enough to have him for a mate.

Paul   What shall we do?

Kevin   We'll tell Mr Kingston about the game and we'll
            make out to him that we're scared about them
            finding out it's us who've grassed them up.

Paul   We are! They'll kill us if they find out!

Kevin   Which is why Mr Kingston won't tell them. He's all
            right, he'll protect us. Besides, he'll be well happy to
            break up their game, especially when we tell him
            they're playing for money.

Paul   How shall we say we found out?

Kevin   We'll tell him that we accidentally overheard them
            talking about it.

Paul   (*grinning*) This is going to be good! I wish we could
            see their faces when they get caught.

Kevin   We'll still get our revenge. They could even get
            suspended for this and that would be *really* good!

            Kevin and Paul grin at each other.

Scene Eight

*Characters: Andy, Richard, Tony, Jamie, Louise,
Sonia, Natalie.*

*The day of the meeting. In the Food Technology
room. Andy and the other members of Chefs' Club
are busily preparing food. Louise enters, Sonia and
Natalie trail after her.*

Louise (*briskly*) Come on, you two.

Natalie	I only said I'd serve. I don't remember saying I'd set the room up as well.
Louise	Stop complaining.
Sonia	At least we get off lessons.
Natalie	But we have to come back to school tonight for the party.
Louise	Stop moaning and get the plates out of the cupboard.
Natalie	And that's another thing. Why can't we have paper plates? Who's going to wash this lot up?
Louise	Not you, I expect.
Natalie	Correct! It's not in my contract.
Sonia	You haven't got a contract.
Natalie	It's a figure of speech, Sonia, a figure of speech.

Natalie and Sonia go to the cupboard. Louise goes over to Andy.

| Louise | How is it going? |
| Andy | (*flustered*) Okay, I think. |

Richard calls to Andy.

Richard	Tuna or ham?
Andy	What?
Richard	Fillings for the sandwiches.
Andy	Both.
Richard	How many?
Andy	I don't know!

Tony joins Andy and Louise.

Tony	I've got the puddings out of the freezer.
Andy	How am I supposed to know how many sandwiches?
Tony	Did you hear me?
Andy	What?
Tony	Oh, forget it!

Louise Don't worry about the buffet table, we'll sort it out.

Sonia calls from the cupboard.

Sonia Something's burning.

Andy Oh, no! Somebody check the oven, quick!

Jamie rushes to the oven.

Jamie Just in time! It's the sausage rolls but I think we've caught them.

Louise I think we'd better go, we've got tables to set. Come on, Natalie.

Natalie (*sarcastically*) Yes, Miss! Let's go, Sonia, we can't keep Her Majesty waiting.

Louise strides from the room, followed by a sulking Natalie and a giggling Sonia.

Scene Nine

Characters: Andy, Richard, Tony, Jamie, Stuart, Clinton.

A short time later. In the Food Technology room. Andy and his crew are busily working. Stuart and Clinton enter. They are carrying mud-covered bags. Stuart puts his bag on a table, next to a plate of ham sandwiches. He helps himself to the sandwiches.

Stuart Ham, my favourite.

Richard Hands off! And get your filthy bag out of the way!

Stuart ignores him.

Stuart Want one, Clinton? Catch!

Stuart throws a sandwich to Clinton. It lands on the floor. Clinton picks it up, wipes it and eats it.

Tony	You're disgusting.
Clinton	I'm starving.
Stuart	Help yourself, there's plenty of food.
Richard	I told you to move your bag.
	Richard picks up the bag and throws it to the floor.
Stuart	Who said you could move my bag? Did you hear anybody say he could, Clinton?
Clinton	No.
Stuart	Then we'll have to teach him a lesson.
	Stuart and Clinton move menacingly towards Richard, who starts to back away.
Jamie	Andy, quick! There's going to be a punch-up!
	Andy notices what's going on and rushes over.
Andy	Don't start, lads, please. I don't want any trouble.
Stuart	Make him pick my bag up, then.
	Andy picks the bag up and hands it to Stuart, who puts it back on the table. Richard picks up the plate of sandwiches and takes it to the other side of the room.
Jamie	He's well out of order.
Tony	Don't waste your breath. Let's get back to work.
	They all start work again, except for Andy, who pleads with Stuart and Clinton.
Andy	Please, lads, can't you go somewhere else?
Clinton	Stuart said you needed some help.
Andy	No, thanks.
Stuart	But yes if your name's Louise. I get it. I thought we were mates.
Andy	Oh, all right. There's a load of salad to get ready. You can wash the lettuce and cucumber.
Stuart	That's more like it! Right, Clinton, jackets off, sleeves up!

Clinton   (*saluting*) Yes, boss!

*Stuart and Clinton take off their jackets and go over
to the sink area. Andy gets back to work.*

Stuart   You get the stuff and I'll fill the sink.

*Stuart fills the sink with water and adds several
squirts of washing-up liquid. Clinton returns, arms
full of the lettuces and cucumbers.*

Clinton   Do you think they've got enough? What's all that
soap for?

Stuart   He said to wash them, so that's what we'll do.
Shove 'em all in.

*Stuart and Clinton laugh as they they dump all the
lettuces and cucumbers into the soapy water and
start to wash them vigorously.*

Clinton   We need a scrubbing brush.

Stuart   Good idea.

Clinton   The lettuce is falling apart.

Stuart   The cucumbers are going all soggy.

*Stuart holds up a cucumber and calls across to
Andy, who comes over to inspect. He stares in
horror at the soapy mess.*

Stuart   Are these clean enough?

Andy   What *are* you doing?

Stuart   (*innocently*) Washing the salad stuff, like you told us
to.

Andy   Not like that! You know I didn't mean like that!

Clinton   How were we supposed to know?

Stuart   Yeah, washing is washing.

Andy   Don't mess things up for me, Miss Wright will go
mad if I'm not ready on time.

Stuart   It's only a joke.

Clinton   I don't think he knows how to take a joke any more.

Andy   Please, lads.

Stuart	Oh, all right. We know when we're not wanted. Come on, Clinton.
Andy	(*relieved*) I'll see you later.
Stuart	Can we take some food with us?
Andy	Just a couple of sandwiches, don't take a load.

Stuart and Clinton take a couple of sandwiches each.

Clinton	Thanks.
Stuart	We'll sit over in that corner to eat them. Don't mind us.

Stuart and Clinton pick up their bags and go over to the corner. Stuart pauses by a table laden with several plates of ham sandwiches. Andy turns back to his work.

Stuar	Grab those clean tea towels, we can wrap the sandwiches up in them.
Clinton	What for?
Stuart	'Cos I say so. They're for later, for Neil and the lads at the card game.
Clinton	Can I come?
Stuart	No.
Clinton	That's not fair. I reckon if I'm nicking food for it I should be allowed to go.
Stuart	It's not up to me. I shouldn't have told you about it in the first place. Neil doesn't want many people to know in case it gets back to the teachers. Anyway, I don't play, I'm the look-out. Now hurry up and pass us those plates before anybody notices.

Clinton passes a plate at a time to Stuart, who takes the sandwiches, wraps them in the towels and puts them into his bag.

Clinton	That's four plates full. Don't you think they'll notice?
Stuart	So what? We may as well eat a few more as well.

Stuart and Clinton help themselves to yet more sandwiches and go and sit in the corner to eat them.

Clinton   (*smiling*) It was a laugh washing all that salad.

Stuart   Yeah. How about another laugh before we go? Give me one of your football boots.

Clinton   What for?

Stuart   You'll see.

Clinton hands a football boot to Stuart, who reaches into the cupboard behind him and takes out a jar of chilli powder.

Stuart   You put a load of chilli into that tuna thing.

He points to a bowl.

Stuart   And I'll scrape some mud from your boot into it as well, for added flavour.

Stuart and Clinton move cautiously to the edge of the cooking area. Clinton quickly empties the jar of chilli powder into the tuna mix. Stuart adds some mud and he stirs it all up with his hand. Richard notices them.

Richard   What are you doing? Get your filthy hand out!

Stuart   I'm only having a taste.

Richard   You're disgusting!

He calls to Andy.

Richard   Get rid of your mates.

Andy looks up.

Andy   Are you two still here?

Stuart   We're just leaving.

Stuart and Clinton pick up their bags and leave the room. They try hard not to laugh.

Jamie   What shall we do about the tuna mix?

Andy   Give it a good stir, no one will notice.

Jamie   (*shrugging*) If you say so.

Andy	And give the cucumbers a rinse to get the soap off.
Tony	We'll have to throw the lettuce away.

Richard sees the empty sandwich plates.

Richard	They've taken all the ham sandwiches! What are we going to do? There isn't any ham left.
Andy	We'll have to make do with Marmite.
Jamie	Marmite? Nobody will want to eat that!
Andy	There isn't anything else.
Richard	Great buffet this is going to be, Marmite and tuna. What a choice!
Tony	I'm glad *I'm* not eating it.
Andy	There's plenty of sausage rolls and crisps.

They hastily carry on with their preparations.

Scene Ten

Characters: Neil, Stuart, Year Eleven pupils 1–3.

Lunchtime of the same day. In Room Five. Stuart is piling ham sandwiches on to a tea towel which he has spread over a table top. Neil enters.

Neil	Haven't you got any plates?
Stuart	Beggars can't be choosers.
Neil	Where is everybody?
Stuart	I don't know, it's your card game.
Neil	I expect they're late coming out of dinner, they'll be here soon.

The door opens and three Year Eleven boys walk in. Neil is relieved to see them. He speaks to Stuart.

Neil   Told you.

He speaks to the boys.

Neil   All right?

Pupil 1   All right.

Neil   I thought we'd sit over there.

Neil points to a table. The boys ignore him and remain standing. Neil points to the sandwiches.

Neil   Have a sandwich.

Pupil 2   I've just had my lunch.

Neil   Put one in your pocket for later.

Pupil 3   (*aggressively*) Are you deaf? We don't want a sandwich.

Stuart   Is this it, just these three? I thought you said there'd be loads.

The Year Eleven Pupils notice Stuart.

Pupil 1   I know him, he's in Year Nine. What's he doing here?

Neil   He's helping out.

Pupil 2   Haven't you got anybody of your own age to hang about with?

Pupil 1   Yeah, he's just a kid.

Pupil 3   He's right, though. Where *is* everybody?

Neil   I don't know, I can't understand it.

Pupil 1   You're useless, Fisher. This happened the last time you tried to organise a game.

Stuart   Did it?

Pupil 2   We said then we'd never come to another one.

Stuart   You mean I gave up my lunch hour and got all those sandwiches for nothing?

Neil   There are still five of us.

Stuart   Not me. I haven't got any money, plus I'm supposed to be look-out.

Pupil 3   That leaves four of us. We'll just have to double the stakes.

Pupil 2   And to make sure it's fair, we've brought along our own cards.

Neil   (*worried*) No, there aren't enough of us to play.

Pupil 3   We can't help that, you invited us.

Pupil 1   Let's start the game. We'll sit at that table over there.

Pupil 2   Keep guard, Davis, like you're supposed to.

Pupil 3   Close the door and stand outside in the corridor. Don't come in unless we tell you, or you see a teacher coming. Got that?

Stuart   Yeah.

Pupil 1   Put your money on the table, Fisher. I think I'll have one of those sandwiches now.

Pupil 2   Good idea, my lunch is beginning to wear off.

The pupils grab a couple of sandwiches each, go over to the table and sit down. They are followed by a reluctant Neil, who slowly puts his money on the table. Pupil 1 takes a pack of cards from his pocket.

Scene Eleven

Characters: Neil, Stuart, Year Eleven Pupils 1–3, Mr Kingston.

A few moments later. Stuart heaves a sigh of relief and opens the door on to the corridor. He looks down the corridor and sees Mr Kingston. Stuart turns back into the room and hastily bangs the door shut. The others look up, startled by the noise.

Stuart   Quick! It's Kingston and he's heading our way!

Pupil 3   Oh, no, that's all we need! Grab a few more sandwiches, Davis, and bring them over here!

Stuart grabs some sandwiches, takes them to the card table, pulls up a chair and sits down nervously. Pupil 1 quickly puts the playing cards back into his pocket. Neil scoops up his money, a pound coin falls unnoticed to the floor. Neil returns the rest to his pocket.

Pupil 1   Stay cool and don't look so nervous, Fisher. Eat a sandwich.

The door opens and Mr Kingston enters.

Mr Kingston   Ah, Fisher, Davis, a little bird told me I might find you here. What's going on?

Stuart   Nothing, Sir.

Neil   We're just having a sandwich with the lads.

Pupil 2   Do you want one, Sir? Help yourself.

Pupil 2 points to the table laden with sandwiches. Mr Kingston looks at them in surprise.

Mr Kingston   There's enough here for an army. Expecting a crowd, are you?

Neil   No, Sir, just us. Stuart brought the sandwiches.

Mr Kingston   Did he, now? And where did you get that little lot from?

Stuart	I made 'em, Sir, at home, Sir.
Mr Kingston	(*sarcastically*) How generous of you. However, I heard that it was something more than a picnic that you would be having here today. I heard that you would be playing cards, for money.
Pupil 3	(*innocently*) Us, Sir? No, Sir.
	Neil looks at Stuart who frowns back at him and shakes his head slightly.
Neil	I don't know what you mean, Sir. There are no cards here.
Mr Kingston	I can see that for myself. It seems that I either arrived too late, or too early. Well, it's a lovely day and we don't want you missing the best of the sunshine. I suggest that you get yourselves out to the playground for some fresh air.
Pupil 1	Yes, Sir. Come on, lads.
	The Year Eleven pupils get quickly to their feet and leave the room. Neil and Stuart start to follow them.
Mr Kingston	Not so fast, you two. You can get this room sorted out, ready for afternoon school. Stuart, wrap all those sandwiches up in the tea towel. I'll take them to the Staff Room till the end of school. You can come and collect them from me then.
Stuart	Yes, Sir.
Mr Kingston	Neil, put the tables straight.
	Stuart picks up the sandwiches from the card table and takes them across to the big pile. He wraps the whole lot up in the tea towel. Neil straightens up the tables. Mr Kingston watches them. As Neil moves a table, Mr Kingston notices the pound coin. He bends down and picks it up and holds it out to the boys.
Mr Kingston	Did either of you happen to drop any money on the floor?
	Neil and Stuart glance at each other quickly.
Stuart	It's not mine. I spent all my money at lunchtime.

Neil It's not mine either.

Mr Kingston That's funny, perhaps it got there by magic. Don't think you've fooled me for one minute, because you haven't and I'm going to be watching you both like a hawk. I'll put this money into the school charity box. Don't forget to collect your sandwiches at the end of school. Right, off you go.

Neil and Stuart leave the room followed by Mr Kingston, who is carrying the sandwiches.

Scene Twelve

Characters: Andy, Louise, Natalie, Sonia, Miss Wright, Mr Kingston.

Early evening of the same day. In the Dining Hall. The buffet is displayed on a long table at one end of the room and there are several other tables arranged around the rest of the room. Miss Wright, Mr Kingston and the pupils are standing in a group by the buffet.

Miss Wright This all looks great. Well done, team!

Andy The girls got the room ready.

Natalie I'm starving. Can I have something to eat?

Louise No!

Andy We've put all the food in sections, sandwiches and salad and stuff, then puddings.

Mr Kingston I think I owe you an apology, Andy. I told Miss Wright that I didn't think you'd pull it off.

Miss Wright That just shows you how much you know!

They all laugh. Miss Wright makes a closer inspection of the buffet.

Miss Wright	It all looks lovely. The cucumber slices that you've used for decoration really sparkle under the lights.
Andy	Mmm.
Miss Wright	There are rather a lot of tuna fish sandwiches.
Mr Kingston	Good, they're my favourite. Can I try one now?
Natalie	No! If I can't, you can't.
Mr Kingston	Fair enough. What kind are those?

He leans across the table.

Mr Kingston	Marmite? That's a strange choice.
Miss Wright	Marmite? Where are the ham sandwiches?
Andy	We lost the ham, Miss. We looked everywhere for it and we couldn't find it.
Mr Kingston	Wait a minute. This wouldn't have anything to do with Stuart Davis by any chance?
Andy	Stuart, Sir? No, Sir.
Mr Kingston	He didn't happen to come by earlier, when you were getting the food ready?
Andy	Err . . .
Mr Kingston	I think I can solve this little mystery. I'll be right back.

Mr Kingston rushes off. Miss Wright stares after him, mystified.

Miss Wright	What's going on?
Andy	Don't know, Miss.
Sonia	I can hear clapping.
Louise	That means the entertainment is finishing. They'll be here soon.
Natalie	Just let me have one sandwich.
Louise	No, it'll spoil the display.
Miss Wright	Never mind, Natalie, I'm sure there'll be enough left over.

The pupils laugh and take up their positions. Miss Wright walks over to greet the guests.

Scene Thirteen

Characters: Andy, Louise, Natalie, Sonia, Miss Wright, Mr Kingston, Mr Freeman (the Deputy Head), Ms Roberts (MP).

A few moments later. The Dining Room is beginning to fill up with guests and pupils who have taken part in the entertainment. Miss Wright greets Ms Roberts, who is being escorted into the room by Mr Freeman. Andy, Louise, Natalie and Sonia are standing behind the buffet table.

Mr Freeman   I must say, this is all looks rather splendid.

Ms Roberts   I couldn't agree more. The entertainment was first class and the supper promises to be of the same high standard.

Miss Wright   Thank you. It was Andy and his team who did all the hard work.

Ms Roberts   Mr Freeman was telling me that there are just four of them.

Miss Wright   That's correct. Richard, Jamie and Tony are around, somewhere, serving drinks. Andy is over there by the buffet. The girls standing next to him volunteered to help out.

Mr Freeman   If you'll just excuse me for a moment, I must address the assembled guests.

Ms Roberts   Certainly.

Mr Freeman claps his hands, loudly.

Mr Freeman   Ladies and gentlemen, pupils, if I could have your attention for a moment. I would like to apologise for the absence of our Headteacher, who has been called away on urgent business, so you're all going to have to put up with me.

The guests laugh.

Mr Freeman   I would also like to thank all those who have
                 worked so hard to make such a success of this
                 gathering. I would now like to ask Ms Roberts, our
                 MP, to lead the way to the buffet.

                 *The guests applaud politely and start to form an
                 orderly queue behind Mr Freeman and Ms Roberts.*

Natalie   Just one slice of cucumber won't hurt.

                 *Natalie reaches out and takes a slice of cucumber.
                 Louise tries to slap her hand away.*

Louise   Natalie!

                 Natalie speaks with her mouth full of cucumber.

Natalie   Aagh, it's horrible! It tastes all soapy.

                 *Andy tastes a slice of cucumber, grimaces and
                 swallows it hastily.*

Andy   It tastes all right to me.

Sonia   Ssh, here come the guests.

                 *Mr Freeman and Ms Roberts approach the table and
                 inspect the food.*

Ms Roberts   This all looks jolly nice, what's this? Tuna, my
                 favourite *(pause)* and Marmite, how interesting.
                 I think I'll have tuna, please.

                 *Ms Roberts holds out her plate and Natalie puts four
                 small tuna sandwiches on it.*

Natalie   Cucumber?

Ms Roberts   Yes, please.

Andy   How about some chicken and salad as well?

Ms Roberts   No, thanks, this is plenty.

                 *Ms Roberts takes her plate over to one of the tables
                 and sits down. Mr Freeman, who has piled his plate
                 as high as he can, follows her.*

Andy   She didn't take very much.

Natalie   All the more for us later.

The rest of the guests start helping themselves to food. Andy watches Ms Roberts carefully. She puts a slice of cucumber into her mouth and frowns. She pretends to cough, reaches into her bag, takes out a tissue, holds it to her mouth, spits the cucumber into it and puts the tissue back into her bag. Andy sighs and turns back to the buffet.

Mr Freeman   Is everything all right?

Ms Roberts   Yes, I've just got a tickle in my throat.

Ms Roberts takes a bite of tuna sandwich and chokes. Tears come into her eyes. She continues to eat the rest of the sandwich quickly, pours a glass of water from the jug that is on the table and takes a big gulp.

Mr Freeman   Is there anything wrong?

Ms Roberts   No, no.

Mr Freeman bites into a tuna sandwich. He splutters and spits it out on to his plate.

Mr Freeman   You didn't eat one of these, did you?

Ms Roberts   I'm afraid I did. I didn't want to make a fuss, especially after the cucumber.

Mr Freeman   What's wrong with the cucumber?

Ms Roberts   (*embarrassed*) It has a strong soapy taste.

Mr Freeman   I'm so sorry! I'll go and have a word with Miss Wright.

Ms Roberts   Not on my behalf, please. I'm sure the rest of the food is fine.

Mr Freeman   You are too kind, Madam. I am so sorry!

Mr Freeman goes to find Miss Wright. Meanwhile, back at the buffet table, Natalie can no longer resist the tuna sandwiches. She quickly pops one whole into her mouth. She shouts in horror.

Natalie   Oh, my god!

Several guests look at her in surprise. Natalie grabs

a plate and spits out the rest of the sandwich.

Louise   Natalie! Stop making a fuss, everyone is staring!

Natalie   (*shouting*) Don't eat the tuna! It's disgusting, don't eat it!

Miss Wright hurries over to the buffet table. Mr Freeman arrives at the same time.

Miss Wright   Natalie, for goodness sake!

Natalie   I can't help it, Miss. It's disgusting.

Mr Freeman   She's quite right. This is most embarrassing. I couldn't eat mine, either. Unfortunately Ms Roberts ate the whole of hers. We must stop the rest of the guests. Somebody get those sandwiches off the table!

Sonia   It's too late, Sir. Look!

They all look out at the rest of the room. Several guests are choking and spluttering. Some are taking huge gulps of water and some are spitting food out on to their plates.

Miss Wright   Oh, no! Andy, where are you?

Andy   It's not my fault. Anyway, soapy cucumber won't hurt you.

Mr Freeman   (*angrily*) It's not the cucumber, you fool! It's the tuna!

Miss Wright   What soap?

Mr Kingston enters the room carrying the ham sandwiches still wrapped in their tea towel. He reaches the buffet table and puts down the sandwiches.

Mr Kingston   What going on? Why are people coughing?

Miss Wright   (*distressed*) It's awful! I've never been so humiliated in my entire life!

Natalie   Don't eat the tuna, Sir! It's really hot and disgusting!

Mr Freeman   Thank you, Natalie, I think you've made your point.

He turns to Mr Kingston.

Mr Freeman	It seems that there's something very wrong with the tuna, not to mention the cucumber.
Andy	It's not my fault, Sir, honest. I mean, I didn't know they'd use washing-up liquid and I don't know anything about the tuna.
Miss Wright	(*screeching*) Washing-up liquid?
Mr Kingston	Who? No, let me guess, Davis and Fisher.
Andy	No, Sir, just Stuart. Oh, and Clinton.
Mr Freeman	What's going on?
Mr Kingston	I'll explain later. In the meantime, let's rescue this situation. Louise, get rid of those tuna sandwiches. Sonia, unwrap that tea towel and put the contents on to a clean plate.
	Louise hurries off with the sandwiches. Sonia unwraps the tea towel. Andy stares in surprise.
Andy	My ham sandwiches!
Mr Freeman	Are they safe to eat?
Andy	(*offended*) Yes, Sir. I made most of them myself.
	Natalie turns to the guests still waiting in the queue for food and smiles politely.
Natalie	I'm afraid the tuna's off, there's ham instead. Oh, I nearly forgot. Don't eat the cucumber.
	Miss Wright and Mr Freeman look at each other in despair.

Scene Fourteen

Characters: Miss Wright, Mr Kingston, Sonia, School Secretary.

The next morning before school. On a corridor. Miss Wright and Mr Kingston are so involved in their discussion that they don't notice Sonia.

Sonia   Miss, Sir, I've got a message from Mr Freeman. He wants . . .

Sonia realises they are not listening and listens in to their conversation.

Miss Wright   I should have taken your advice and put someone else in charge.

Mr Kingston   You weren't to know that Stuart would get involved. Andy's no match for him.

Miss Wright   None of them seem to be able to stand up to him.

Mr Kingston   Mmm, it's getting beyond a joke. He needs taking down a peg or two. A few minutes later and I would have caught him and Fisher out. I'm certain they were about to start playing cards for money.

Miss Wright   How did you know?

Mr Kingston   Andy's younger brother told me. He overheard Davis and Fisher plotting.

Miss Wright   Mr Freeman questioned Andy about the food. He told him that Stuart and Clinton went to the Food Technology room and created havoc. They stole the ham sandwiches.

Mr Kingston   Yes, to provide a buffet for Fisher and his mates.

Miss Wright   Not only that, they wrecked the lettuce and cucumber and doctored the tuna mix. I checked my cupboard and there's a jar of chilli powder missing.

Miss Wright suddenly notices Sonia.

Miss Wright   (*sharply*) Yes, Sonia, what do you want?

Sonia	I've got a message from Mr Freeman. He said could you both go to his office at morning break?

Before either of them can reply, the School Secretary comes running up to them.

School Sec. (*breathless*) Thank goodness I've found you. I've got an urgent message.

Miss Wright (*anxiously*) What is it?

School Sec. It's to do with your guest last night, Ms Roberts.

Miss Wright Yes?

School Sec. We've just had a phone call from the hospital. It appears that she became very ill a couple of hours ago and they have admitted her for tests. They want to know what she had to eat last night. Could you phone them and let them know?

Miss Wright and Mr Kingston look at each other in horror.

Miss Wright Oh, no! I'll come straight away!

Mr Kingston I'll come with you.

They rush off down the corridor. Sonia stares after them in amazement.

Scene Fifteen

Characters: Andy, Gordon, Louise, Natalie, Sonia, Stuart, Clinton, Mrs Powers, Miss Wright.

A few minutes later. At the back of the Registration room. Louise and Natalie are telling Gordon about the evening's events. Andy listens gloomily.

Gordon (*laughing*) I don't believe it! They really used washing-up liquid?

Natalie It's not funny, we could have died.

Louise Stop exaggerating. Andy's upset enough as it is.

Gordon That's his fault.

He speaks to Andy.

Gordon I told you not to be friends with him any more.

Andy How was I to know he'd cause all that trouble?

Sonia rushes into the room.

Sonia (*excitedly*) You'll never guess what I've found out!

Louise What?

Sonia sits down.

Sonia Wait a minute, let me get my breath back.

Natalie Hurry up, tell us!

Sonia They've only gone and taken that Ms Roberts woman into hospital!

They all stare at Sonia, shocked.

Louise You're joking!

Sonia No, it's true. I heard the Secretary tell Miss Wright. She's got to go and phone the hospital. They think it's something she ate.

Andy (*panicking*) Oh, no! What am I going to do? They'll blame me! What if she dies?

Gordon Your food's bad but not that bad.

Natalie Don't joke! You didn't taste that terrible tuna stuff. Ms Roberts ate a whole sandwich of it. I'm glad I spat mine out now!

Sonia But it was Stuart and Clinton who poisoned the tuna.

Louise What do you mean, poisoned?

Sonia They put a load of chilli powder into it. I heard Miss Wright tell Mr Kingston.

Gordon That won't poison you.

Natalie How do you know? Ms Roberts might have a sensitive stomach.

Stuart and Clinton enter the room.

Stuart   Who grassed me up, then?

Gordon   What are you going on about?

Stuart   Kingston found out about the card game. Lucky for us, it hadn't started. He tried to get us to own up but we were too sharp for him.

Sonia   None of us grassed you up.

Stuart   (*suspiciously*) How do you know?

Sonia   'Cos I do, that's all.

Louise   You're really in trouble this time, both of you.

Natalie   Yes, a really important guest is in hospital, dying because she ate some of that tuna stuff you poisoned!

Clinton   I . . .

Stuart interrupts quickly.

Stuart   We don't know what you're talking about, do we, Clinton?

Clinton doesn't reply.

Sonia   (*furious*) Don't lie! I heard Miss Wright tell Mr Kingston all about it.

Stuart   How did she find out?

Andy   I told them about you washing the cucumber. I didn't know about the tuna.

Sonia   Mr Kingston found out you stole the ham sandwiches and when Miss Wright noticed her chilli powder had gone missing she guessed what you had done.

Stuart   Yeah, it's only a guess. She can't prove anything. Anyway, a bit of chilli powder won't hurt anyone.

Clinton   What about the mud?

Stuart   Shut up!

Louise   What mud?

Clinton   He scraped the mud off my football boot into the tuna. I only put the chilli in.

Gordon	You're disgusting!
Stuart	Do they know about the mud?
Sonia	No, they didn't mention mud.
Stuart	That's all right, then. They can't prove a thing.
Louise	I think we'd better tell Mrs Powers about this at Registration.
Andy	I thought you didn't grass.
Louise	This is different. There could be something in the mud that is poisonous.
Natalie	This might turn into an epidemic!
Gordon	You're really for it now, Davis.
Sonia	And you, Clinton.
Clinton	Not me! It wasn't my idea!
Louise	You didn't have to do what he told you.
	Mrs Powers enters the room and goes to her desk. She looks worried.
Mrs Powers	Stuart, Clinton, Mr Freeman would like to see you both immediately.
	Louise and Stuart whisper together.
Louise	They know.
Stuart	Not about the mud.
Mrs Powers	What's that you're saying? I can't hear you.
Stuart	Nothing, Miss.
Louise	Mrs Powers, can I talk to you privately?
	Mrs Powers regards Louise seriously.
Mrs Powers	Yes, come to my desk.
	Louise walks slowly towards Mrs Powers' desk. Clinton looks at the floor. Stuart watches her furiously. Before she reaches the desk, the door opens and Miss Wright bursts in.
Miss Wright	Mrs Powers, about that small matter we were discussing earlier.
Mrs Powers	Yes, I was just about to . . .

Miss Wright	(*interrupting*) The panic's over. It seems that Ms Roberts has appendicitis!
	Mrs Powers and Miss Wright smile at each other in relief.
Mrs Powers	That *is* good news!
Miss Wright	Yes, isn't it?
Mrs Powers	Excuse me a moment. Louise, you had something you wanted to tell me.
	Louise turns and looks back at the others. She hesitates and then turns back to Mrs Powers.
Louise	It's okay, it's not important. It's just about my options. I'll tell you another time.
Mrs Powers	If you're sure.
	Louise nods.
Mrs Powers	Stuart, Clinton, I thought I had told you to go to Mr Freeman's office.
	Stuart tries to look puzzled.
Stuart	I don't understand, Miss.
Mrs Powers	I think you do. It's a small matter of some ham sandwiches, not to mention some tuna and cucumber.
	Stuart and Clinton sit in silence.
Mrs Powers	Don't just sit there, get along to Mr Freeman's office immediately.
Clinton	Yes, Miss. Come on, Stuart, we may as well get it over with.
	The others watch as Stuart and Clinton slowly leave the room.

The End

Stuart

List of Characters

Year Nine pupils

Stuart

Clinton

Andy

Gordon

Louise

Natalie

Sonia

Rosemary

Year Eleven pupils

Neil, Stuart's friend

Omar, a music pupil

Year Seven pupils

Kevin, Andy's brother

Paul, Kevin's friend

Teachers

Mr Kingston, French/PE

Mrs Powers, Form Tutor

Mr Freeman, Deputy Head

STUART

Scene One

*Characters: Stuart, Clinton, Andy, Gordon, Louise,
Natalie, Sonia.*

*Monday lunchtime. In the Registration room. Stuart
and Clinton have returned to school after being
suspended for a week for sabotaging Andy's buffet
at a school function. Stuart is questioning Sonia
about how Mr Kingston knew he had been involved
in organising a card game just before he was
suspended. Clinton is looking on. Andy is sitting apart
reading a magazine and trying to ignore them all.*

Stuart   Who grassed me up?

Sonia   I don't know what you're talking about.

Clinton   Give it a rest, this is only our first day back after
being suspended.

Stuart   (*ignoring him*) You said that you heard Mr Kingston
telling Miss Wright that somebody had told him
about overhearing me and Neil talking about
organising a card game.

Sonia   I'm not telling you.

*Stuart bangs his fist down hard on the table. Sonia
jumps in alarm and backs away.*

Stuart   (*shouting*) Tell me!

Sonia   (*frightened*) No!

Clinton   Leave her alone.

Stuart   I've got a right to know. You'd want to know if
someone was going round listening in to your
conversations.

Clinton Drop it, you'll only get into more trouble.

Louise and Natalie enter.

Louise Who's in trouble?

Natalie What's going on?

Sonia is relieved to see Louise and Natalie. She goes to stand next to them.

Sonia He keeps trying to make me tell him who told Mr Kingston about the card game.

Louise Don't you know when to stop? Isn't it enough that you were suspended for a week?

Stuart That wouldn't have happened if it hadn't been for him and his stupid buffet!

Stuart points aggressively to Andy, who looks up from his magazine.

Andy I didn't know you'd put stuff in the tuna and I didn't tell them about the sandwiches. Mr Kingston found those. I only told them about you washing the cucumber in soap.

Stuart But we never owned up to the tuna, did we, Clinton?

Clinton They knew anyway.

Stuart They didn't know about the mud and they didn't know for certain that we put the chilli in.

Louise I should have told Mrs Powers. They might have expelled you rather than just suspending you.

Stuart You would have liked that, wouldn't you?

Louise Yes!

Louise and Stuart glare at each other. Clinton changes the subject.

Clinton Where's Gordon?

Natalie He's at a football meeting.

Andy Oh, no, I was meant to go to that meeting, they're picking the first team today! I forgot all about it.

Stuart They wouldn't pick you, you're useless. Anyway, I thought you didn't go to football.

Andy	(*gloomily*) I do now there's no more Chefs' Club. Miss cancelled it.
Louise	That's a shame.
Andy	I don't mind. I don't want to be a chef any more.
Sonia	But you're a good cook.
Andy	I can't handle all the organising. It does my head in.

Gordon enters the room. He is grinning.

Natalie	Did you get it?
Gordon	Yes! You are looking at the captain of the First Team!
Sonia	That's brilliant!
Gordon	How would you girls like to be my cheer leaders?
Louise	The short skirts would look better on you boys.

They all laugh, except for Stuart, who glares at them angrily.

Andy	I forgot to come to the meeting.
Gordon	That's all right, you wouldn't have been picked.
Natalie	Gordon, that's not nice!
Andy	I don't mind. I'm useless at football.
Clinton	Has Mr Kingston picked the whole team?
Gordon	Nearly.
Clinton	I didn't know about the meeting, 'cos of being suspended. Do you think if I went to see him, he'd give me a place?
Gordon	You've been to all the practices so it's worth a try.
Stuart	That's a good idea. We'll go and see Kingston after school.
Gordon	Who mentioned you?
Stuart	You don't pick the team.

Stuart and Gordon glare at each other in hostility. Stuart takes a step towards Gordon, who stands his ground. Natalie hastily intervenes and puts her hand on Gordon's arm.

Natalie　Let's go to lunch.

Louise　Good idea. Are you coming, Sonia?

Stuart stands aside as Natalie, Louise and Gordon leave the room, followed by Sonia. As she walks by, Stuart blocks her path and threatens her menacingly in a low voice.

Stuart　I'll get you when you're on your own and then you'll tell me who grassed me up.

Sonia is too frightened to reply. She hurries out of the room.

Sonia　Wait for me, Louise!

Scene Two

Characters: Stuart, Clinton, Neil, Mr Kingston.

Later the same day after school. In the corridor, outside the Sports Hall. Stuart and Clinton are waiting for Mr Kingston. Neil joins them.

Stuart　How's it going?

Neil　Boring. What are you doing here?

Stuart　Waiting for Kingston to see if there are any places left in the football team.

Neil　Now you're back you can help me organise another card game.

Stuart　(*sarcastically*) Yeah, like the last one.

Neil　It wasn't my fault the rest of the lads couldn't make it. Just as well, seeing as how Kingston found out about it.

Stuart　Somebody grassed us up.

Neil	Who?
Stuart	Don't know yet but I'm working on it.
Neil	Let me know when you find out and we'll sort 'em. See you later.

Neil strolls off down the corridor. Stuart and Clinton watch him go.

Clinton	He thinks he's so hard.
Stuart	He's a laugh.
Clinton	It's funny how he doesn't seem to have any mates except for you. Every time you see him, he's on his own.
Stuart	He's got mates.

Mr Kingston comes out of the Sports Hall.

Clinton	Can we talk to you, Sir, about the football team?
Mr Kingston	Why didn't you attend the meeting at lunchtime?
Clinton	We didn't know about it.

Mr Kingston pretends to remember.

Mr Kingston	Oh, yes, you were out of school last week when the notice went up.
Clinton	Yes, Sir.
Mr Kingston	(*relenting*) It just so happens that I was considering you, Clinton. However, it will depend upon your behaviour in the future. The members of the football team must be seen to be setting a good example to the rest of the school.
Clinton	Yes, Sir.
Mr Kingston	The younger ones look up to you.
Clinton	Yes, Sir.
Mr Kingston	Let's see how you settle back into school and I'll think about it.
Clinton	(*relieved*) Thanks!
Mr Kingston	And what do you want, Davis?

Stuart	Same thing as him. We . . .
Mr Kingston	(*interrupting*) You've been involved in several incidents recently. I'm not sure that I can trust you to behave.
Stuart	(*muttering*) Suit yourself.
Mr Kingston	What did you say? Speak up, boy.
Stuart	(*louder*) I'll behave myself . . . Sir.
Mr Kingston	I don't know. I'm going to have to think about it. Both of you come and see me this time next week and I'll give you my answer.
Clinton	Yes, Sir. Thanks, Sir.
	Mr Kingston goes back into the Sports Hall.
Stuart	*'Yes, Sir. Thanks, Sir.'* Crawler!
Clinton	I want to be in the team and if you want to be in it, you should watch your mouth.
Stuart	It won't make any difference, he hates me. You're in, I'm out.
Clinton	You don't know that. Let's wait till next week.
Stuart	I'm telling you. You're in, I'm out.

Scene Three

Characters: Mr Kingston, Mrs Powers, Mr Freeman.
Tuesday morning before school. In the Staff room.

Mr Kingston	I've got no problem with putting Clinton into the team, I think he's learned his lesson. It's the other one, Davis, that bothers me.
Mr Freeman	What do you mean?

Mr Kingston	It's nothing I can put my finger on, it's a sort of, *'I know it all and I can get away with anything,'* type thing.
Mrs Powers	He used to be such a pleasant boy. He needs to get away from Neil Fisher's influence.
Mr Freeman	The Fisher boy concerns me. He doesn't seem to have any real friends, just temporary hangers-on, who hero-worship him for a while and then see through him.
Mrs Powers	Like Stuart, you mean?
Mr Kingston	That's the trouble, Stuart can't see through him. He's picking up some bad habits.
Mrs Powers	Maybe if he had a more positive focus, something to use up his energy and keep him out of mischief.
Mr Kingston	(*smiling*) I get the message, Mrs P. I should put Stuart in the football team.
Mr Freeman	It might not hurt to give him the benefit of the doubt, one last chance.
Mr Kingston	Mmm, you've got to laugh, fancy washing the cucumber with soap. It's like something from a sit-com.
Mr Freeman	If you do put him in the team, you'll have to keep a careful eye on him.
Mr Kingston	I've arranged to meet them both next Monday, I'll let them sweat it out till then.
Mr Freeman	Good idea, keep me posted.
	They start to gather their belongings ready for morning school.

Scene Four

Characters: Stuart, Neil.

Friday lunchtime. Behind the Science Block. Stuart and Neil are sharing a cigarette.

Neil Found out who grassed us up yet?

Stuart I'm still working on it.

Neil (*grumbling*) Get a move on, we can't set up another game till we know. It's too risky.

Stuart I can't do another game. I've already been suspended, you haven't.

Neil Losing your bottle, are you? Tell you what, I'll split the profits with you.

Stuart (*doubtfully*) I don't know.

Neil (*disgusted*) And I thought you were well hard.

Stuart I want to be in the football team.

Neil (*shrugging*) Go and play your kiddie games if you want. It makes no difference to me, I'll find a new partner.

Stuart Do you really mean it about splitting the profits?

Neil Yeah, this is just the beginning. I know where we can get hold of some pirate videos to sell off cheap. You can make loads of money if you stick with me.

Stuart All right. It's Sonia who knows who grassed on us.

Neil Find her today and get back to me so we can sort something out.

Stuart (*looking at his watch*) What's the time? One o'clock, she might be in a music practice room. She has flute lessons on Fridays.

Neil Don't hang about, go and find her. It shouldn't take too long.

Stuart Right! I'll meet you here after school.

Neil   And it's your turn to splash out on the fags, you're
            always smoking mine.

Stuart Yeah, yeah. See you later.

            *Stuart hurries off to the Music Block. Neil finishes the
            cigarette and stubs it out.*

Scene Five

Characters: Stuart, Sonia, Omar, Rosemary.

*A few minutes later. In the Music Block. There is the
sound of instruments being played. Stuart opens the
door of the nearest practice room. Omar is playing
the piano.*

Omar   Get out!

Stuart   Have you seen Sonia?

Omar   No! Go away, I'm busy.

Stuart   All right, all right, don't lose your rag.

              Stuart backs out of the door.

Omar   Close the door!

              *Stuart closes the door and opens the next one.
              Rosemary is playing the guitar.*

Rosemary What are you doing here? This isn't your scene.

Stuart   I'm looking for Sonia. I've got a message for her
              from Mrs Powers.

Rosemary Try next door.

Stuart   Thanks.

              *Stuart closes the door and tries the door of the next
              practice room. Sonia is standing in front of a music
              stand practising scales on her flute. She has her*

back to the door and doesn't hear Stuart. He
watches her for a moment, enters the room and
closes the door quietly. He creeps up behind her.

Stuart   Boo!

Sonia jumps, turns round and almost drops her flute
when she sees Stuart. She carefully puts the flute on
a nearby table and looks at Stuart apprehensively.

Sonia   Oh, it's you.

Stuart   I was passing by and I heard you playing your flute
so I thought I'd pay you a visit.

Sonia   Liar. What do you want?

Stuart   It's about who grassed up me and Neil.

Sonia   I might have guessed.

Stuart   Tell me.

Sonia   No.

Stuart   Why not?

Sonia   'Cos it wouldn't be fair and you might hurt them.

Stuart   So there's more than one.

Sonia   I'm not telling you, Stuart, so just go away.

Stuart   Go on, it makes no difference to you.

Sonia   No.

Stuart   I promise I won't hurt them, whoever they are.

Sonia   Louise didn't tell Mrs Powers about the mud you put
in the tuna mix at Andy's buffet, so why should I tell
you who heard you talking about your stupid card
game?

Stuart   Somebody heard us talking? They couldn't have
unless they were hiding. Let me think . . .

He thinks out loud to himself.

Stuart   Me and Neil were having a fag. I'd just nicked
Kevin's ball . . .

Sonia   This is stupid. I've said too much already. *Please* go
away.

Stuart   Kevin! It was Kevin! Him and his mate must have followed us. It was him, wasn't it?

Stuart triumphantly punches the air and starts to pace around the small room. He absent-mindedly picks up Sonia's flute.

Stuart   Yes!

Sonia   Give me my flute.

Stuart   What?

Stuart examines the flute with interest.

Sonia   Please give it back.

Stuart   I'll give it back if you tell me I'm right. That it was Kevin and his mate.

Sonia   No!

Sonia makes a sudden grab for the flute but Stuart snatches it out of her reach and holds it high above his head. Sonia tries hard not to cry.

Stuart   (*laughing*) You're not getting it back until you tell me.

Sonia is too distressed to speak. Stuart turns his attention back to the flute.

Stuart   It's just a load of old metal. Who bought you this?

Sonia   My dad, it's not new.

Stuart   Still, I bet it cost a lot.

Sonia doesn't answer. Stuart takes a step towards her threateningly. He raises his voice.

Stuart   I bet it cost a lot! Didn't you hear me?

Sonia   (*frightened*) Yes.

Stuart   Answer me, then. I wonder what would happen if I hit it against the table.

Sonia   (*miserably*) I don't know.

Stuart   Would you like to find out?

Stuart taps the edge of the table with the flute.

Sonia   No, please don't!

Stuart   So tell me.

Sonia doesn't answer. Stuart holds the flute above his head again.

Stuart   I'm going to count to three and if you don't tell me, I'm going to bash your flute against this table. One . . . two . . .

Stuart swings his arm back.

Sonia   All right, I'll tell you! It was Kevin and his friend, Paul.

Stuart   I was right! Me and Neil will get 'em for this!

Sonia   Give me my flute back.

Stuart   What? Oh, yes, your flute. Say, please.

Sonia   Stuart!

Stuart   Say, please.

Sonia   Please.

Stuart gives the flute back to Sonia who takes it from him and clutches it tightly.

Sonia   (*tearfully*) Stuart, *please* don't hurt them.

Stuart   Grow up, Sonia. I haven't got time to hang about here listening to you moan on. I've got things to do.

Stuart leaves the room.

Stuart   See you around. Thanks for the information.

As Stuart leaves the room he collides with Rosemary.

Rosemary   Oi, watch it!

Stuart laughs and runs off down the corridor. Rosemary notices a very distressed Sonia through the open doorway.

Rosemary   Are you all right? Did the message from Mrs Powers upset you?

Sonia   What message?

Rosemary   Stuart said he had a message for you from Mrs Powers.

Sonia	No, yes, I don't know.
	Sonia bursts into tears and sits down on a chair.
Rosemary	I'd better get someone.
Sonia	No, I'll be all right. I can't find my tissues.
	She rummages around in her bag.
Sonia	Louise and Natalie will be here in a minute.
Rosemary	(*doubtfully*) If you're sure . . .
	Rosemary looks along the corridor and is relieved to see Louise and Natalie.
Rosemary	Thank goodness you're here! Sonia is ever so upset. Stuart gave her a message from Mrs Powers. I think it's really bad news.
	Louise and Natalie rush to the open door of the practice room.

Scene Six

Characters: Sonia, Louise, Natalie, Rosemary.

The same time. The same place. Louise and Natalie stare at Rosemary in astonishment. They notice Sonia who is hunched over the table crying. Louise pushes past Rosemary and goes to comfort Sonia. Natalie and Rosemary remain standing in the open doorway.

Louise	(*anxiously*) What's wrong? Tell me!
	Sonia continues to cry and doesn't answer. Louise looks across to Rosemary.
Rosemary	It's like I said. Stuart brought her a message from Mrs Powers.

Sonia sits up and pushes her hair from her face.

Sonia   (*angrily*) He didn't!

Rosemary   That's what he told me.

Sonia   It was horrible! He shouted at me and tried to break my flute!

Natalie   What? Where is he, I'll kill him!

Sonia   He made me tell him! I didn't want to but he made me!

Rosemary   Tell him what?

Sonia   And now he'll hurt them and it's all my fault.

Sonia starts to cry again. Natalie moves further into the room, followed by Rosemary.

Sonia   He knows it's Kevin.

Rosemary   Kevin? That's Andy's little brother.

Louise   I think you'd better go, Rosemary. This is private business.

Rosemary   No, I'll stay, you might need some help.

Natalie   (*rudely*) Your sort of help means telling the whole school. Go away!

Louise   Please go, Rosemary.

Rosemary   Oh, all right.

Louise   And don't tell anybody about this.

Rosemary   As if I would!

Rosemary leaves the room and closes the door behind her.

Natalie   It'll be all over the school in half an hour.

Louise   She didn't hear much so there's nothing to tell. Sonia, you've got to tell us what happened.

Sonia   Stuart made me tell him who grassed him up. I had to, he said he would break my flute if I didn't.

Natalie   You mentioned Kevin.

Sonia   It was him and his friend, Paul. They overheard

Stuart and Neil planning a card game.

Natalie   Stuart will slaughter them!

Louise   He wouldn't be so stupid, he'd get expelled.

Sonia   I don't think he cares about that. He was really angry. What shall we do?

Natalie   We'll get Gordon and some of his mates to sort them out.

Louise   Then Gordon will get into trouble. That won't solve anything.

Natalie   But we've got to do something! They can't go around bullying all the time!

Louise   We'll have to tell a teacher.

Sonia   (*frightened*) Oh, no, Louise! They'll come after me!

Louise   This is too serious to handle by ourselves. Stuart has already bullied you and if we don't stop him, he'll move on to Kevin and Paul. You don't want that, do you?

Sonia   No.

Natalie   She's right, Sonia. The teachers have always told us we need help to stop bullies.

Louise   They'll know what to do.

Sonia   Who shall we tell?

Louise   Mr Kingston. He knows Stuart well.

Natalie   We'll go to the Sports Hall and see if we can find him.

Louise   It's the end of lunch now. We'll have to go later, after school finishes.

Natalie   I'll help you pack your things away.

Natalie helps Sonia pack away her flute and music. Louise gets a crumpled but clean tissue from her pocket and hands it to Sonia, who smiles. The girls leave the room.

Scene Seven

Characters: Sonia, Louise, Natalie, Mr Kingston.
The same day, after school. Outside the Sports Hall.
Mr Kingston is locking the Sports Hall door. He is
surprised to see the three girls.

Mr Kingston   Haven't you three got homes to go to?

Louise   Can we have a word with you, Sir?

Mr Kingston looks at his watch.

Mr Kingston   Right now?

Natalie   It's really important, Sir. It's about Stuart Davis and
Sonia.

Mr Kingston   (*smiling*) I'm surprised at you, Sonia. I thought you
had better taste.

Louise   This isn't funny, Sir. You can see she's upset.

Mr Kingston regards Sonia, who looks back at him
miserably. He becomes more serious.

Mr Kingston   I'm sorry, I didn't mean to joke. What's wrong?

Natalie   Stuart has been bullying her. Tell him, Sonia!

Mr Kingston   Yes, I think you'd better.

Sonia   I heard you telling Miss Wright that Kevin and Paul
told you about Stuart and Neil's card game.

Mr Kingston   Go on.

Sonia takes a deep breath.

Sonia   Well, he found out that I knew and made me tell
him.

Mr Kingston   (*angrily*) He did what?

Louise   It was worse than that! He shouted at her and
threatened her and said he would break her flute.

Natalie   He got her on her own in a music practice room
and when we found her she was really upset and

crying and now she's scared of what will happen.

Sonia Louise said it would be best to tell you but I'm scared they'll come after me.

Mr Kingston You did the right thing. You can leave this to me, I'll sort Stuart Davis and Neil Fisher out.

Sonia But what if they come after me? What if they get Kevin and Paul?

Mr Kingston They won't! I'll make sure of that. By the time I've finished with them they'll know what it's like to be on the receiving end and they will be too frightened to approach you! Anyway, nothing can happen over the weekend and I'll see them first thing on Monday morning.

Louise I'm glad we did the right thing and told you. We'll stick together until this is sorted out.

Mr Kingston I also want you to tell your parents and if they're at all concerned, they can phone me on Monday – mid-morning would be best. By then I will have seen our two bully boys.

Sonia Yes, Sir.

Mr Kingston I think you three had better go home. It's getting late.

Louise 'Bye, Sir.

Mr Kingston 'Bye, girls. Have a good weekend and try not to worry.

Mr Kingston walks away. The girls watch him go.

Scene Eight

Characters: Stuart, Neil.

Sunday afternoon. The school pond. Stuart and Neil approach the pond cautiously. Stuart is carrying a plastic carrier bag in one hand and a full black refuse sack in the other. Neil is carrying a shovel and a pair of garden shears.

Stuart Are you sure no one saw us?

Neil Yeah, you get the place to yourself on a Sunday afternoon. The caretaker will be sleeping off his lunch.

Stuart Have you been here before on a Sunday?

Neil Loads of times. Is this the pond, then?

Stuart Yeah, little Kevin and his Year Seven mates have spent ages doing it up. It's their special project for some sort of competition they're going in for.

Neil It's well posh.

Stuart It won't be by the time we've finished with it.

Neil I still say we should have beaten them up. It would have been a lot easier.

Stuart And get caught? Don't be stupid, we'd get expelled. This way we teach 'em a lesson and get away with it.

Neil (*laughing*) They'll be well gutted.

Stuart That's the general idea.

Neil How can we be sure they'll know it's us who trashed their precious pond?

Stuart We'll leave a clue. I've still got Kevin's tennis ball.

Stuart takes the tennis ball from his bag and holds it up for Neil to examine.

Neil They all look the same. How will he know it's his?

Stuart He's not stupid, he can add up two and two and make four. Let's get to work, we haven't got all day.

Stuart rummages around in the carrier bag and pulls out a large bottle of bleach, a tin of red paint and a screwdriver.

Neil What shall I do?

Stuart Dig up all the plants around the edge of the pond, break them up and scatter them about the place. I'll tip this bleach into the water. That should kill off some wildlife.

Neil What's the paint for?

Stuart I thought I'd paint the grass and chuck the rest in the water.

Neil starts digging. Stuart unscrews the bleach bottle top, empties the bleach into the water and throws the empty bottle in as well. He uses the screwdriver to open the tin of paint and splashes the contents over the grass at the edge of the pond.

Stuart Chuck the dirt into the pond.

Neil See that little wall they've built?

Neil points to a small wall that edges part of the pond. Stuart nods.

Neil Smash it up and chuck the bricks in the water!

Stuart (*laughing*) Yeah!

Stuart smashes up the wall. Neil uses the garden shears to cut through some bushes. They continue to destroy the pond and the surrounding area for several more minutes. Finally they stop and survey the damage admiringly.

Neil That'll teach 'em! They won't win any competition now. Let's go before somebody comes.

Stuart Hang on, just a couple more things to do.

Stuart drags the refuse sack to the destroyed and muddy edge of the pond and opens it. It is full of household rubbish. He takes out a couple of bottles, smashes them and scatters the glass. He tips the rest of the rubbish plus the plastic sack into the pond.

Stuart And now for the tennis ball.

He carefully places the ball in a prominent position next to a brick and some broken glass. He glares angrily for a moment at the wreckage and then turns away abruptly.

Stuart Let's go!

Stuart strides off. Neil collects up the shovel, shears and screwdriver and runs to catch him up.

Neil Wait up!

Scene Nine

Characters: Stuart, Clinton, Gordon, Natalie, Sonia, Mrs Powers.

Monday morning. The Registration room. Sonia and Natalie are sitting at a table. Gordon enters. Sonia whispers to Natalie.

Sonia You haven't said anything to him, have you?

Natalie No, don't worry.

Sonia I can't help it, I'm really scared.

Gordon What are you two plotting?

Natalie Nothing.

Gordon throws his bag on to the floor and sits down next to them. Sonia stares miserably at the table.

Gordon No need to look so happy, Sonia, even if it is the start of another week in paradise.

Natalie   Shut up! She's got a lot on her mind.

Gordon   Like what?

Before Natalie can reply, Stuart and Clinton enter. Sonia groans.

Sonia   Oh, no.

Stuart pauses by their table and glares at them without saying anything. He goes over to a table on the opposite side of the room and sits down. Clinton follows him.

Clinton   What was all that about?

Stuart   What?

Clinton   If looks could kill, they'd be dead by now.

Stuart   I hate them. They think they know it all.

Mrs Powers enters the room looking harassed.

Mrs Powers   Ah, there you are, Clinton, Stuart. I'm glad you're nice and early. Mr Kingston wants to see you both right away. You'll find him in the PE office.

Clinton stands and picks up his bag. Stuart remains seated and glares across the room at Sonia.

Clinton   Don't you want to be in the football team?

Stuart   Oh, yeah, I forgot.

Stuart stands, picks up his bag and starts to follow Clinton out of the room. They are almost at the door when Mrs Powers calls them back.

Mrs Powers   I don't suppose either of you knows anything about the awful thing that happened to Year Seven's pond?

Natalie   What happened, Miss?

Mrs Powers   At some point over the weekend it was completely destroyed.

Gordon   (*shocked*) That's terrible, who would do a thing like that?

Mrs Powers	That's what we want to find out. The Head has asked all Form Tutors to speak to their groups this morning at Registration. I don't want to delay you two boys but I thought I'd better mention it in case you're not back when I speak to the whole class.
Clinton	I don't know anything about it, Miss. Do you, Stuart?
Stuart	No. When did it happen?
Mrs Powers	The caretaker thinks some time on Sunday. Let me know if you hear anything.
Clinton	Yes, Miss. Let's go, Stuart, we don't want to be late.
	Stuart and Clinton leave the room at the same time as Andy and Louise are entering.
Stuart	Hi, Andy.
	Andy doesn't reply and turns his back on Stuart, who shrugs his shoulders as he leaves.
Louise	What was all that about? I thought you two were mates.
Andy	He's no mate of mine.
Louise	You're learning at last.
Natalie	Did you hear about what happened to Year Seven's pond? Mrs Powers just told us.
Mrs Powers	I must have left my glasses in the staff room. I'll be back in a minute.
	Mrs Powers leaves the room.

Scene Ten

Characters: Sonia, Natalie, Louise, Gordon, Andy.
The same time. The same place. Andy and Louise
sit down next to the others.

Andy   I know all about it.

Louise   About Mrs Powers' glasses?

Andy   No, about the pond.

Gordon   Somebody trashed it.

Louise   That's awful! Who'd do a thing like that?

Natalie   How do you know about it, Andy? Mrs Powers only told us a minute ago.

Andy   My brother built it with his mates. We saw it on our way into school. It's a right mess, he's well gutted.

Sonia   Your brother, Kevin?

Natalie   Don't be stupid, he's only got one br . . . (*realising*) Oh, no! You don't think . . .

Louise   Yes, I do.

Sonia   So do I.

Louise, Natalie and Sonia look at each other in horror.

Gordon   Will someone tell me what's going on?

Louise   We'd better tell them, Sonia.

Sonia nods.

Natalie   Stuart made Sonia tell him that it was Kevin and his mate Paul who had grassed him and Neil up. He was really horrible to her. He shouted at her and threatened her and everything.

Gordon stands up angrily.

Gordon   Why didn't you tell me? I'll kill him.

Louise   We didn't tell you because we didn't want you to get into trouble. We told Mr Kingston, he'll sort them out.

Gordon sits down again.

Gordon   What's this got to do with the pond?

Sonia   Don't you see? It's Kevin's pond, Stuart must have trashed it.

Andy   That's funny, that's what Kevin reckons as well. He was going on about a tennis ball.

Natalie He should tell Mr Kingston!

Andy   Yeah, I'll have a word with him at break.

Gordon   Wait till I get Davis. He won't know what day it is!

Natalie No, Gordon! If you hit him, they'll suspend you.

Sonia   They'll kick you off the team and it will be my fault. I've caused enough trouble already. I never should have told Stuart.

Louise   From what you told me, he didn't give you much choice.

Gordon   What exactly happened? Tell me from the beginning and don't leave anything out.

Natalie Well . . .

The girls start to tell Gordon what happened.

Scene Eleven

Characters: Stuart, Clinton, Neil, Mr Kingston.
Five minutes later. Outside the PE office. Neil is leaning against the wall. Stuart and Clinton join him.

Stuart   What are you here for?

Neil   Same thing as you.

Clinton I didn't know you were interested in football.

Neil	Who's talking about football?
Clinton	We're here to find out if we've been picked for the team.
Neil	That's nice.

Neil looks at Stuart and they exchange wary glances. Mr Kingston arrives.

Mr Kingston	I'll speak to you first, Clinton. Come into the office. You two wait here.

Mr Kingston unlocks the office door and enters, followed by Clinton.

Stuart	Do you think he knows about the pond?
Neil	Knows? Everybody knows. It's all over the school.
Stuart	Well, they don't know it was us.
Neil	Keep your voice down!

Stuart lowers his voice.

Stuart	Don't tell him anything. Let him do all the talking.

The door opens and Clinton leaves the room, a big grin on his face.

Clinton	Thanks, Sir.
Mr Kingston	Remember what I said, don't let me down. Tell the others to come in.
Clinton	I'm in the team! He said to go in. Yes!

Clinton does a little dance along the corridor and punches the air with his fist. Stuart and Neil go into the office.

Mr Kingston	Right, you two. What do you know about the school pond?
Stuart	It's been trashed.
Mr Kingston	Correct. Do you know who did it?
Stuart	No, Sir.
Mr Kingston	Fisher?
Neil	No, Sir.
Mr Kingston	A little bird told me it might have been you two.

The boys don't reply.

Mr Kingston I didn't hear you. Speak up.

Neil We don't know anything about it, do we, Stuart?

Stuart No.

Mr Kingston I think you do. Let's start at the beginning, shall we? For example, I know, Davis, that you bullied Sonia into telling you that it was young Kevin and his friend who told me about your card game plans. What have you got to say for yourselves now?

The boys don't reply.

Mr Kingston I'm waiting for an answer.

The boys still don't reply. Mr Kingston leans back in his chair.

Mr Kingston I know, Davis. *I know* about your disgraceful treatment of Sonia. What's more, Mr Freeman knows, the Head knows and Sonia's parents know, and if you go anywhere near her you will be instantly suspended with a view to expulsion. Do I make myself clear?

Stuart Yes.

Mr Kingston Yes, Sir.

Stuart Yes, Sir.

Mr Kingston So you admit to bullying her?

Stuart All right, so I had a go at her.

Mr Kingston *'Had a go at her.'* What sort of answer is that? You were out of order and you know it!

Stuart Yes, Sir.

Mr Kingston Which brings me to the small matter of the pond. You found out about Kevin, and you and Fisher decided to seek your revenge by destroying his pond.

Neil We never, Sir!

Mr Kingston Have you any idea how much work they put into

building that pond just so that hooligans like you
could come along and wreck it in a few minutes?

Stuart   We had nothing to do with the pond, Sir, honest. I
admit to having a go at Sonia but we didn't wreck
no pond. I didn't even know about it until Mrs
Powers told me.

Neil   Yeah, and then Stuart told me while we were
waiting to see you.

Mr Kingston regards them both thoughtfully.

Mr Kingston   I think you are both lying. I think you did destroy the
pond but I can't prove it. I will though, I will. Make
no mistake, you won't get away with this.

*Mr Kingston and Stuart look at each other for a
moment. Stuart looks away first.*

Neil   Can we go, Sir? It's nearly first lesson.

Mr Kingston   You're not usually so keen, Fisher. Yes, you can go.
Davis, stay behind.

*Neil leaves the office. As he goes, he mutters to
Stuart.*

Neil   I'll see you at Break, usual place.

Mr Kingston speaks to Stuart.

Mr Kingston   I think you've probably guessed by now that you're
not in the team. I don't want you at the practices
either.

Stuart doesn't reply.

Mr Kingston   And as punishment for bullying Sonia, litter duty
every break and lunchtime for a week.

Stuart   Sir!

Mr Kingston   You heard.

Stuart   That's not fair!

Mr Kingston   Oh, yes it is, Davis. Oh, yes it is. You can go now.

*As Stuart leaves the office, Mr Kingston sighs to
himself and shakes his head.*

Scene Twelve

Characters: Stuart, Neil, Gordon, Kevin, Paul.

Monday morning Break. On the playground. Stuart is walking slowly across the playground trailing a refuse sack behind him. He is wearing rubber gloves. Every so often he stops to pick up a piece of litter which he puts into the sack. Kevin and Paul watch him from a safe distance.

Paul How do you know for sure it was him?

Kevin 'Cos he left the tennis ball he nicked off me next to a load of bricks and glass.

Paul Have you told a teacher?

Kevin There's no point. Tennis balls all look the same. It'll be his word against mine.

Paul He looks a right prat in those yellow gloves.

Kevin Yeah, serves him right.

Gordon approaches Stuart angrily.

Gordon Oi, you! I've heard all about it from Natalie and I'm warning you. If you go anywhere near those girls, I'll get you!

Stuart Think you're hard?

Gordon I can beat you any day of the week.

As he walks away, Gordon throws a half-eaten apple on to the ground.

Gordon Make yourself useful and pick that up!

Neil watches him go and then joins Stuart. He points at the refuse sack.

Neil So this is why you couldn't meet me.

Stuart (*gloomily*) Yeah.

Neil Never mind, it's a small price to pay.

Stuart	It's not you that has to do it twice a day for a week.
Neil	They didn't find out about the pond though.
Stuart	I hate 'em! I hate 'em all, especially Kingston. He's really got it in for me!
Neil	Get your own back, then.
Stuart	Oh, yeah, and how am I supposed to do that?
Neil	Listen, I've got an idea. Kingston's working late tonight. He always does on a Monday.
Stuart	How do you know?
Neil	I just know these things. Anyway, he parks his car in the back car park.
Stuart	So?
Neil	So there's never anybody around at that time. We could let his tyres down.
Stuart	What? You're mad!
Neil	How will they find out it's us? They didn't find out about the pond. They won't be able to prove a thing.
Stuart	Yeah, it might work.
Neil	All we have to do is make sure the coast is clear.
Stuart	Right, you're on!
Neil	I'll meet you by the back gate about six o'clock. Leave your bike in the bike shed. If anyone sees us we can say we've come back to get it.
Stuart	Good idea. I'll see you later.
Neil	Those gloves really suit you.
Stuart	Watch it!

Stuart waves the refuse sack at Neil, who laughs and runs off.

Scene Thirteen

Characters: Stuart, Neil.

Monday evening. In the back car park. Stuart and Neil are crouching behind a car.

Stuart   Can you see anybody?

Neil pops his head up and takes a good look round. He stands up.

Neil   No, it's all clear.

Stuart stands up.

Stuart   Which car is Kingston's?

Neil   (*pointing*) That red one over there.

Stuart   That heap of junk?

Neil   (*laughing*) Yeah, we'll be doing him a favour. You let the tyres down and I'll keep guard.

Stuart and Neil run to Mr Kingston's car. Stuart crouches down next to the driver's side front wheel, takes off the dust cap and lets the tyre down. Neil stands behind him, keeping guard. Stuart moves on to the back wheel. He doesn't see Neil take a screwdriver from his pocket and make a deep scratch along the side of the car. Stuart goes to the other side of the car. Neil follows him, dragging the screwdriver along the side of the car as he goes. Stuart lets down the other two tyres. Neil quickly puts the screwdriver back into his pocket before Stuart turns round to face him.

Neil   Quick, let's get out of here!

Stuart   I've just got to get my bike. I'll catch you up.

Neil runs off towards the school gates. Stuart runs to the bike shed, gets on his bike and rides off after Neil.

Scene Fourteen

Characters: Mr Freeman, Mr Kingston, Stuart, Neil.
Tuesday morning. Mr Freeman's office. Mr Kingston
is very angry. Mr Freeman is trying to calm him
down.

Mr Kingston   Did you see the scratches?

Mr Freeman   Yes.

Mr Kingston   They're really deep. It's going to cost a fortune to put right.

Mr Freeman   Can't you claim it on your insurance?

Mr Kingston   And lose my no claims bonus? No, thanks. Wait till I get my hands on them!

Mr Freeman   You won't solve anything by being so agitated. The main thing is that we've caught them.

Mr Kingston   It's not your car! It was bad enough having to call out the AA to pump the tyres back up. That was just inconvenient but those scratches are going to cost me a lot of money!

Mr Freeman   They will be here in a minute. They won't have had time to talk to each other and get their stories straight. That's why I waited until the middle of second lesson before sending for them. I've staggered their arrival so that they won't meet each other on the way.

Mr Kingston   They'll find out soon enough!

Mr Freeman   It's important to remain calm so that they don't know *how* we found out. We'll let them drop themselves in it.

There is a knock at the door.

Mr Freeman   Come in.

Neil enters. He is surprised to see Mr Kingston.

Neil	You wanted to see me, Sir.
Mr Freeman	Yes, Neil. Take a seat.
	Neil sits down. Mr Freeman looks over some papers. Mr Kingston looks out of the window. A couple of minutes pass. Neil fidgets in his chair nervously. There is another knock on the door. Mr Freeman looks up from his papers.
Mr Freeman	Come in.
	Stuart enters. Mr Kingston turns from the window and glares at him. Stuart looks across questioningly at Neil, who shrugs his shoulders.
Mr Freeman	Take a seat, Stuart. Mr Kingston and I have some questions we would like to ask you both.
	Stuart sits down.
Mr Freeman	Would you like to begin, Mr Kingston?
Mr Kingston	Thank you. Do either of you know anything about certain events that took place in the back car park yesterday evening?
Stuart	No, Sir.
Mr Kingston	Fisher?
Neil	No, Sir.
Mr Freeman	Are you both quite sure? Think very carefully.
Neil	I don't know what you are talking about.
Mr Kingston	Where were you both yesterday at around say, six o'clock in the evening?
Stuart	I was at home, Sir, having my tea.
Neil	And me.
Mr Freeman	You were at Stuart's house, having tea?
Neil	No, Sir. I was at my house.
Mr Kingston	So neither of you would know how my car tyres were let down?
Stuart	Were they? No, Sir.
Mr Kingston	Yes, they most certainly were. Not only that, my car was badly scratched in several places. I would say

	that someone dragged some sort of sharp instrument along the sides.
Mr Freeman	And you're both quite sure that you know nothing about the incident?
Neil	Yes, Sir.
Mr Freeman	Stuart?
Stuart	I don't know anything either.
Mr Freeman	Then I'm sure you won't mind if we play you a short video extract from a film that was taken by the security camera that overlooks the back car park.

Stuart and Neil exchange horrified glances.

Mr Kingston	(*triumphantly*) Gotcha', Davis!

Stuart stands up and turns angrily to Neil.

Stuart	You told me no one would see us!
Mr Freeman	Sit down, Stuart.

Stuart remains standing.

Neil	How was I to know they'd be filming us?
Stuart	You said you knew everything about this place.
Neil	I didn't know there was a camera. Anyway, there might not be, they might be tricking us.
Mr Freeman	I can assure you that this is no trick. We've got it all on film. While Stuart was letting down the tyres you, Neil, were scratching the car with what looks suspiciously like a screwdriver.
Stuart	I didn't know that! I didn't know he was scratching the car, honest! All right, I let the tyres down but I never did no damage.
Mr Kingston	(*angrily*) No damage! How dare you! What do you call letting tyres down? What do you call destroying the school pond? What do you call sabotaging an important school function? I think that's enough damage to be going on with, don't you?
Mr Freeman	(*quietly*) Leave this to me.
Mr Kingston	With pleasure!

Mr Freeman	I am sure that you both realise how serious the matter is. The Police have been informed.
Stuart	No!
Mr Freeman	I'm afraid so, Stuart. They have already been to the school to survey the damage and they have taken the security video away with them as evidence.

Stuart turns to Neil. He is furious.

Stuart	It's all your fault! I should never have listened to you.
Mr Kingston	It's too late for that, Davis. It's about time you took responsibility for your own actions.
Mr Freeman	For the last time, Stuart, sit down.

Stuart sits down, dejectedly.

Mr Freeman	Your parents have been informed and they are at this moment talking to the Head, who will be telling them that it is their duty to make an appointment to take you to the Police Station for further questioning. Mr Kingston and I will take you to the Head's office now.
Neil	What will happen to us?
Mr Freeman	I can't say for sure. As soon as the Head has spoken to you both, you will be escorted from the premises. It will be a matter for the Governors to decide but I am sure that the Head will recommend expulsion. The criminal procedures will be in the hands of the Police.
Mr Kingston	Come along, let's get this over with.

Stuart and Neil leave the office, followed by Mr Kingston and Mr Freeman.

Scene Fifteen

Characters: Louise, Natalie, Sonia, Gordon, Andy, Clinton, Rosemary.

Lunchtime of the same day. In the Registration room. Louise and Sonia are doing their homework. Natalie and Gordon are talking quietly together. Andy is resting his head on a table top, dozing. Clinton is reading a football magazine. Rosemary rushes into the room. They all stop what they are doing and look up.

Rosemary	You'll never guess what! Stuart and Neil are going to be expelled!
Louise	What?
Natalie	I don't believe it!
Andy	Yes!
Gordon	What for?
Clinton	You're joking!
Rosemary	I'm not joking! Ella saw them come out of the Head's office with their parents.
Louise	What have they done?
Sonia	Is it about the pond?
Rosemary	What pond? Oh, *that* pond. No, it's much juicier than that.
Natalie	Hurry up and tell us!
Rosemary	They trashed Mr Kingston's car.
Sonia	No!
Rosemary	Yes! They were caught by the security camera. The car's a right mess. The Police have been called and everything.
Gordon	How do you know?

Rosemary	I've got my methods. You just have to know the right people to ask, that's all. Got to go, Nigel and Omar don't know yet.
	Rosemary rushes out of the room.
Gordon	Amazing!
Louise	I never thought I'd be glad that Rosemary is such a gossip.
Clinton	Stuart has really messed up big time. He'll be lucky to find another school.
Gordon	Fisher won't. He's leaving this year anyway.
Sonia	That means he won't be able to do his GCSEs.
Andy	Some people have all the luck.
Natalie	Andy!
Andy	I'm useless at exams.
Sonia	You're a good cook.
Andy	No, I'm not. I'm useless at everything. Gordon and Clinton are good at football and you girls are really clever.
Natalie	Louise might be, I'm not.
Andy	And you all know what you want to do when you leave school.
Sonia	I haven't got a clue.
Clinton	Me neither.
Gordon	I might not be good enough to be a professional footballer.
Louise	My mum says that if you want to see your dreams come true, you have to be determined and have a lot of luck along the way.
Sonia	Your mum's full of good advice. Where does she get it from?
Louise	My Grandma. Let's go to lunch.
Natalie	Lunch! I'm starving!
	They all laugh as they leave the room together.

The End

SPEAKING AND LISTENING ACTIVITIES

Help Notes can be found on pages 167–168.

LOUISE

INDIVIDUAL (Help Notes 1)

1 Friendship. Prepare and give a short talk on what makes a good friend.

Points you might consider:
- loyalty
- sharing
- being honest with each other.

PAIRS (Help Notes 2)

2 The end justifies the means. Louise truants to try to help Steve. Have a discussion about 'doing the right thing but in the wrong way'.

Points you might consider:
- other people's feelings
- breaking the rules
- telling the truth
- doing things 'your way'.

3 Sports. Discuss the differences between team sports and individual sporting activities.

Points you might consider:
- character building
- individual ability
- team spirit
- fitness
- achievement
- 'cheating'.

GROUP (Help Notes 2)

4 School uniform. Discuss the pros and cons of having a school uniform and a policy about hair length, jewellery, nail polish, etc.

Points you might consider:
- cost
- comfort
- school image
- personal image.

WRITING BASED ON ORAL ACTIVITIES

You can choose writing activities from this section that are based on oral work that you have done, or on the oral work of others that you have heard and made notes on. However, you can also choose activities for which you have had no oral preparation.

5 Imagine you are going to take part in a debate for and against school uniform. Choose which side of the argument to support. Make sure you include comments that will address points the opposition might raise. *(Help Notes 3)*

6 Write a story called 'The Friends'. *(Help Notes 5)*

NATALIE

INDIVIDUAL (Help Notes 1)

1 The music scene. Prepare and give a short talk on your favourite music, pop star or group.

Points you might consider:
- why you like the music
- what you like about the performers
- things that you collect
- concerts you have been to.

PAIRS (Help Notes 2)

2 Magazines. Interview each other about your favourite magazines.

Points you might consider:
- contents
- layout
- cost
- favourite sections.

GROUP (Help Notes 2)

3 Creating the right image. Discuss the pressures that make some young people worry too much about their appearance and weight to the point where it becomes a problem.

Points you might consider:
- peer group pressure
- the influence of TV, films and magazines.

4 A school disco. Plan a school disco. Think about:
- venue
- advertising
- ticket selling
- type of music
- decorations
- security.

WRITING BASED ON ORAL ACTIVITIES

You can choose writing activities from this section that are based on oral work that you have done, or on the oral work of others that you have heard and made notes on. However, you can also choose activities for which you have had no oral preparation.

5 Design a leaflet advertising a school disco. *(Help Notes 6)*

6 Write a report for your school magazine about the points made during the discussion about creating the right image. *(Help Notes 4)*

ANDY

INDIVIDUAL (Help Notes 1)

1 My dream meal. Prepare a short talk on your 'dream meal'.

Points you might consider:
- where and with whom would you be
- menu
- number of courses and which you would enjoy most.

PAIRS (Help Notes 2)

2 Gambling. Discuss your opinions about gambling.

Points you might consider:
- gambling for money
- casinos
- slot machines
- addiction
- the Lottery.

GROUP (Help Notes 2)

3 Peer group pressure. Someone younger than you is being influenced too strongly by a friend. What would your advice be?

Points you might consider:
- trusting your own opinion
- the desire to be the same as everyone else
- coping with rejection
- standing up for yourself.

4 'Grassing Up'. Louise almost told Mrs Powers about Stuart and Clinton's activities but at the last minute she changed her mind. Did she make the right decision or are there times when 'telling' is the right thing to do?

Points you might consider:
- friendship and loyalty
- preventing future bad behaviour
- being responsible for others.

WRITING BASED ON ORAL ACTIVITIES

You can choose writing activities from this section that are based on oral work that you have done, or on the oral work of others that you have heard and made notes on. However, you can also choose activities for which you have had no oral preparation.

5 Write a story called 'You didn't have to do what he/she told you'. (*Help Notes 5*)

6 Design a leaflet encouraging young people to eat healthily. (*Help Notes 6*) Think about:
- the health benefits
- eating healthily on a budget
- making food look attractive
- where to get help and information.

STUART

INDIVIDUAL (Help Notes 1)

1 The future. Prepare a short talk about what you think your life will be like in the future and what you might like to do.

PAIRS (Help Notes 2)

2 The Reunion. Each of you chooses to be a character from the play who is meeting the other for the first time in ten years. Have a conversation.

GROUP (Help Notes 2)

3 Bullying: A school policy. Discuss all aspects of what should be included in a school policy designed to combat bullying.

Points you might consider:
- feeling safe
- someone to talk to
- where to go for help
- punishments for bullies.

4 Tobacco advertising. Does the government have the right to ban tobacco advertising, or is such a policy against individual freedom?

Points you might consider:
- the right to choose
- tobacco-related illness
- making cigarette smoking attractive
- government health warnings.

WRITING BASED ON ORAL ACTIVITIES

You can choose writing activities from this section that are based on oral work that you have done, or on the oral work of others that you have heard and made notes on. However, you can also choose activities for which you have had no oral preparation.

5 Design a poster that could be used in an anti-bullying campaign for schools. Decide what information you will include, and make it eye-catching.

6 Write a letter to yourself about your hopes and dreams for the future. Put it in a sealed envelope and do not open it until ten years from now.

HELP NOTES

1 INDIVIDUAL ORAL WORK

- Prepare well, and practise and time your talk.
- Don't write out the whole talk, or read it, or learn it off by heart.
- Use notes, and visual aids.
- Speak to the whole class, not just to the teacher, and try to stand still.
- Use a good vocabulary and avoid slang.
- Speak clearly and loudly for the whole of your allowed time.

2 PAIRS AND GROUP ORAL WORK

- Prepare well, have interesting content, and a good vocabulary.
- Divide the time equally between yourselves and listen carefully to one another.
- Encourage others to take part, especially those who are not saying much.
- Have a sensible seating arrangement and be aware of your audience.

3 DISCURSIVE (ARGUMENTATIVE) WRITING

- Use different sources for your information, such as magazines, newspapers, videos, surveys.
- Some argumentative work will require you simply to state the facts For and Against. Or you may be asked to give your own opinion as well. Make sure you understand what you are being asked to do.
- Keep the facts separate from your opinions and have a brief introduction.
- In your conclusion briefly bring the main points together and, if required, give your own opinion.

4 REPORT WRITING

- Collect all the information you need and arrange it into categories.
- A report is not an essay. You can use sub-headings, graphs, lists and short points.
- A report uses formal language to state the facts. It may have a conclusion or recommendations at the end.

5 STORY WRITING

- Have a brainstorming session and jot down all the ideas that your title suggests to you.
- Work out your plot/storyline.
- Thing about your characters. Imagine what they would look like, how they would think, speak and act.
- Try to use vivid language that describes a place, a person's feelings, or a moment of tension or excitement.
- Have a strong structure – a good beginning, middle and end.

6 LEAFLET WRITING

- Remember that all the information has to go on one piece of paper.
- It is a good idea to fold the paper into three to get maximum coverage without it looking as though there is a great deal to read.
- It must be eye-catching, quick and easy to read, but must contain all the essential information.
- Think about using short headlines, bullet points and illustrations.
- Include a contact name, address, and telephone number for any replies.